The natural history of a survey

An account of the methodological
issues encoun
life be

The natural history of a survey

An account of the methodological issues encountered in a study of life before death

ANN CARTWRIGHT and CLIVE SEALE
Institute for Social Studies in Medical Care

King Edward's Hospital Fund for London

© Institute for Social Studies in Medical Care 1990
Typeset by Tradespools Ltd
Printed and bound in England by Hollen Street Press
Distributed for the King's Fund by
Bailey Distribution Ltd

ISBN 1 85551 056 1

King's Fund Publishing Office
14 Palace Court
London W2 4HT

Contents

Acknowledgements

We are particularly grateful to the relatives and friends of the people who died who answered our many questions, often recalling sad and poignant memories to do so. We are also greatly indebted to the general practitioners, consultants and nurses who participated in the study and to the administrators, managers and staff who helped us to identify the doctors and nurses.

Many others contributed to the study: The Office of Population Censuses and Surveys, particularly Pat Hunter and Maureen Hoskins, who provided the sample of deaths; the interviewers on the main and pilot study – Helen Allen, Tessa Bain, Jenny Bell, Irene Boller, Gillian Calder, Sheila Chetham, Joan Gallop, Hilary Gellman, Hilary Golden, Margaret Jones, Josephine Leighton, Jane Malone, Kay Morley, Caroline Morris, Marie Oxtoby, Joan Read, Rita Redston, Ellen Southwell, Jenny Spackman, Ann Start, Ron Thompson, Amanda Thurstone, Gillian Wall, Barbara Walton and Joan Worthington; the coders – Dorothy Goodwin and Margaret Hall; the cardpuncher – Hazel Adams; our statistician – Joy Windsor; our secretary – Heather Taylor; our treasurer – Louis Hancock; Graham Farrow who checked this book; other colleagues who contributed in a variety of ways – Nick Baker, Ann Jacoby, Emma Jefferys, Kathryn McCann, Caroline Plimley and Alwyn Turner; David Metcalfe and David Wilkin at the Centre for Primary Care Research in Manchester who gave us hospitality for our briefings; Colin Murray Parkes who tried to persuade two ethical committees to approve the study; the members of the Institute's Advisory Committee – Abe Adelstein, Tony Alment, Val Beral, Vera Carstairs, May Clarke, Karen Dunnell, John Fox, Austin Heady, Margot Jefferys, Joyce Leeson, John McEwan, Martin Richards, Alwyn Smith, Mike Wadsworth and Jenny Griffin; the Department of Health who gave us additional information about general practitioners and funded AC's salary and the Institute overheads. The Medical Research Council funded CS's salary and the costs of the study.

We are grateful to them all.

1 Conception and fund raising

This book describes the processes of doing a national survey and the frustrations and rewards we experienced. It is a 'nuts and bolts' report, outlining what we tried to do and what happened. Our aim is to tell what doing this particular survey was like and to convey something of the demands, the variety and the payoffs of this type of work. In this chapter I (AC) explain why I wanted to do the study and how I got the money for it. Like many other research projects the ideas for this one developed from earlier work, so I start with something of a history of the projects that led up to it.

Background history

The first study I did at the Institute of Community Studies reflected the consumer orientation of that organisation and my interest in health care. It described the reactions of a nationally representative sample of over 700 patients to their experience in hospital (Cartwright 1964). One of the main interests was in communication and so the views and experiences of a smaller sample of general practitioners were also sought. Looking at a problem from the perspective of both patients and professionals proved rewarding and became a feature of many of my subsequent studies. The role of the general practitioner as seen by both patients and doctors was the subject of my next main study (Cartwright 1967). After this general review of patient-doctor relationships in general practice I felt I wanted to look at a particular topic in more depth and find out about the help patients got, or did not get, from their doctor with a specific problem. The topic I chose was contraception and the sample I took consisted of recent mothers and fathers, and was based on a random sample of births. This enabled me to study a group of people who had made a recent decision, either deliberately or by default, about whether or not to avoid or delay a subsequent pregnancy. I was then able to look at the role general practitioners, health visitors and family planning clinics played in giving contraceptive advice to recent mothers (Cartwright 1970). I got the sample of births* through the General Register Office, and this involved persuading John Boreham, the senior statistician there that it was appropriate for them to do this. He was sympathetic and I

* Strictly maternities as multiple births were just counted once.

1

was delighted and relieved when he agreed. Despite initial anxieties – this was in the late sixties and the contraceptive pill was only recently available – that parents might be reluctant to discuss with strangers a topic that was then seen as very personal, the response rate was good (91% among mothers, 82% among fathers) and the interviewers had little difficulty persuading people to cooperate. The parents had been chosen because they had recently had a baby: they seemed to understand and accept this more readily than people chosen at random from the electoral register for the general practice study. As a statistician this set me thinking about other sampling frames which could be used to illuminate health care issues.

So it was on the basis of the availability of a suitable sampling frame that the first study of life before death (Cartwright, Hockey and Anderson 1973) was conceived.

The first study of life before death

This then was an opportunistic study, but I make no apology for this. In my view researchers *should* take advantage of such opportunities as the existence of sampling frames. They should think about the ways such frames can be used to further their aims and explore the fields they are interested in. I argued that a study based on a random sample of adult deaths in England and Wales could give a picture of the way society cared for a group of people, many of whom would be old and most of whom would be sick, in the year before they died. Because people would not be identified by their needs for care – although clearly many of them would have great needs – the study would show the ways in which a multiplicity of services functioned, or failed to function. With this reasoning I was able to persuade the Department of Health and Social Security to fund the study and the Queen's Institute of District Nursing to second Lisbeth Hockey to work on the study with me.

The nature of the sample determined both the strengths and weaknesses of the study. Because people were only identified after their death we could not interview them and inevitably our information was incomplete. The best we could do was to interview the people who could tell us the most about the last year of the lives of the people who had died. Approaching and identifying them and then persuading them to answer our questions was the most challenging and uncharted part of the study. Death, even more than contraception, was a taboo subject and interviewers had to be persuaded and supported in taking on a task which at least some of them felt initially might be intrusive, unwelcome and unhelpful to bereaved relatives. We sought the advice of Colin Murray Parkes, a psychiatrist involved in bereavement research and counselling. He suggested that while people who were recently bereaved were usually glad of an opportunity to discuss their experiences, after about six months they became more reluctant to do so, but later were again willing to talk and share their experiences. Accordingly, we planned the study so that people were approached either three or nine months after the death.

Interviewers were selected and trained for the study with particular care. They needed not only the usual skills and techniques of interviewing but sympathy for and understanding of bereaved people and the ability to be able to convey these without diverting the course of the interview in a biased way. They also needed to be able to cope with the emotional strains and demands of interviewing bereaved people. The interviewers we chose were rather older than those for our previous studies and a few had a nursing background. They succeeded in interviewing someone about 82% of the sample of 960 deaths.

In addition to interviewing relatives or friends (or in a few cases staff of institutions or other officials) we collected information from general practitioners, district nurses and health visitors involved in the care of dying or bereaved people. The focus of the study was mainly on care at home and in the community, reflecting the interests and concerns of other Institute studies around that time.

The study revealed many inadequacies in services, problems of co-ordination between different types of services, failures of communication, and lack of practical, emotional and social support for the relatives and friends who bore the brunt of caring for the people who died.

Almost twenty years on

The first study of life before death was done in 1969 and less than 1% of that sample of people had died in a hospital or institution which specialised in terminal care. During the nineteen seventies inpatient units for terminal care increased rapidly and home care services and hospital support services were introduced in a number of areas (Lunt 1981 and Taylor 1983). This is illustrated in the graph based on their data.

Figure 1   Growth in terminal care facilities

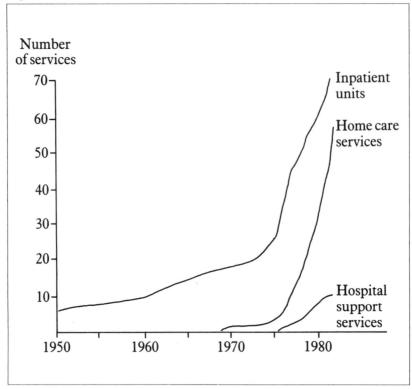

There were no definitive figures on the number of deaths occurring in hospices, Fry (1983) put the figure at 4%, Wilkes (1986) at 5%, Rees (1982) estimated that 7% of people dying of cancer did so in hospices. But no nationally representative survey of the care given to people before their death had been done since our survey in 1969. Taylor (1983) in a review of the role and future of the hospice movement in Britain argued that: 'There is an urgent need to distinguish between the reality of hospice care and the rhetoric which surrounds its successful promotion.' I thought that another survey, like the earlier study of life before death and based on a similar sample, would be an appropriate way to address this issue. In March 1983 I outlined a possible research project: 'Life before death and the impact of the hospice movement' which I sent to the Department of Health and Social Security. But to describe the search for funds for the study, some more background history is needed, this time about the Institute for Social Studies in Medical Care and its funding.

Institute for Social Studies in Medical Care and its funding

In 1970 Michael Young, the director of the Institute for Community Studies and a believer in small being beautiful, decided that the Medical Care Research Unit, which I had established within ICS, was large enough to stand on its own feet and should separate from ICS. So the Institute for Social Studies in Medical Care was set up. At the time we had four project grants (including the one for the first Life for before death study) all from the Department of Health and Social Security, but no other sources of support. Subsequently we obtained project grants from the Office of Population Censuses and Surveys in 1972, from the Social Science Research Council in 1973 and three more from the Department of Health and Social Security in 1973, 1974 and 1975. Then in 1975 we got a rolling grant from the DHSS. This was for six years in the first place but was reviewed every two years, so that effectively the Institute was assured of basic support for between four and six years ahead and would have four years' notice when the grant stopped.

The grant covers our overhead costs and core staff salaries, funds for particular projects being negotiated separately under the Roth-schild (1971) guidelines for research and development. These are based on the customer-contractor principle. The customer (DHSS) says what it wants, the contractor (ISSMC) does it, and the customer pays. In practice, for the majority of ISSMC studies that have been funded by DHSS, the initiative has come from ISSMC, and our first task has been to persuade the DHSS that it would be a useful study which they would like done.

So when we think of a project we want to do, we prepare a brief outline and try to discuss it with the customers at the DHSS and interest them in the project. One reason for just submitting an outline is that it can be modified after discussion, another is that if the Department is not interested we are free to submit it elsewhere. But, if a formal proposal is submitted and rejected on the advice of scientific referees, the Department and the Medical Research Council have agreed that the MRC will not consider it subsequently.

Lack of interest at DHSS

After I sent an outline proposal to the DHSS in April 1983 I received some initial encouragement but eventually, at a meeting in November 1984, I was told that 'the position had changed and now "customers" had indicated that a study on care of the terminally ill would need to be aimed at a different set of problems.' The issues they raised were related to the resources, support and management of home care teams. These would not have needed any survey of the experiences of people who had died and did not seem to me an appropriate field for the ISSMC – from the point of view either of our interests or our skills.

The Medical Research Council

The Institute got its first grant from the MRC in 1982 for a feasibility study: monitoring maternity services by postal questionnaires to mothers. The project went well and we felt our credit with the MRC was good. This encouraged me to approach them about the second study of life before death. Again I sent them an outline of the project first; this was in January 1985. This was discussed at a meeting of the Health Services Research Panel in March who agreed that 'it was an important area of research' and that I should be 'invited to submit a full application.' This I did in April. The project was to be called 'Life before death in 1986' and the proposed starting date was 1st April 1986. The stated aims of the project were:

1 To describe the last year of the lives of a random sample of adults dying in 1986.
2 To make comparisons with the earlier study and identify changes in the nature and availability of care and in the attitudes and expectations of lay and professional carers.
3 To make some assessment of the influence of the hospice movement on these changes.
4 To describe, in more detail than was done in the 1969 study, the institutional care of people in the year preceding their death.
5 To determine the experiences and views of the doctors and nurses involved in the care of these people in the last year of their lives.
6 To describe the care and support given to close relatives both after and before the death.

The basic purpose of these descriptions, comparisons and assessments was to identify ways of improving the quality of life before death.

In outlining the background to the project I pointed out that the earlier study, in the absence of more up-to-date information, was still being used and quoted. And I referenced Taylor (1983), Hinton (1984) and Field (1984).

In addition to the increased emphasis on institutional care another change from the 1969 study was in the way areas for the study were to be selected. In the earlier study registration districts were stratified first by county and London boroughs versus the rest, then by region. In the present study it was planned to stratify them first by the presence or absence of a hospice, and after that by region. This was to ensure that the sample was representative in relation to a key factor: the presence or absence of a hospice.

One anxiety I had was over the interpretation of results, particularly in relation to the assessment of the influence of the hospice movement on any changes between the two studies: there might be other reasons for changes. This was discussed at some length in the proposal.

The proposal was considered by the MRC Neurosciences Board and in August 1985 I heard that the application was approved. But, meanwhile, at the request of the DHSS, I had undertaken another, one year, study to be completed during 1986. I therefore asked the MRC to postpone the start of the study until January 1987 and to change its title to 'Life before death in 1987.' They agreed to these changes.

Reflections on the starting line

The fact that the earlier study had been done made it, I think, easier to get support for the second study. It was clear that it was possible to select a sample from the register of deaths and get cooperation from a relative or friend of most of the people who had died. Because of this I was less anxious about the study and the ability of the ISSMC to do it successfully. Another factor that contributed to my feeling of relaxation, even complacency, over this was being in charge and working in an institute whose sole function was research. In university departments I had found that research was sometimes given a low priority, particularly by secretarial staff and this could make it difficult to keep to timetables. Being in control of resources makes it easier to plan and keep to a schedule, and the more experience one has, the more realistic planning can be.

However, as we shall see, I had not taken into account two things that had changed since the previous study. One of these changes was to result in a substantial modification to the sample design, while the other was to threaten the viability of the study and disrupt its timetable.

Meanwhile, towards the end of 1986 we advertised for a researcher to work with me on the project. Clive Seale was appointed and started in February 1987. He takes up the account in the next chapter on the pilot study.

2 The pilot

The study began with the advantage of having been carried out in similar form some twenty years previously. In a sense, the experience of this earlier study meant that many of the lessons which a pilot study would teach us were known already. The previous study had been based on a random sample of registration districts, taking deaths of people normally resident in those districts. The approach to relatives and others who knew the people who died, by enquiries at the homes of the deceased and those who registered the deaths, had been used successfully in the earlier study. Many of the questions we planned to ask were used on the previous study, so were tried and tested and, for the most part, found to work well. So the sampling strategy, approach and a large part of the questionnaire design were, apparently, known quantities. In these circumstances, why go to the time and trouble of doing a pilot? In the event, the pilot showed us that in a number of important ways the study could not simply be repeated as before. The lessons learned from the 1986 pilot led to changes in the study design, most importantly in the area of sampling, but also in other areas. Nor should the less tangible benefits of a 'dry run' be discounted. The pilot stage of the project was to lead to changes that delayed the study by six months, but without it the main project would not have achieved its aims.

Sampling

The study of deaths in 1969 had been done in twelve randomly selected registration districts in England and Wales. Deaths occurring at all times of the year were sampled, interviewing being staggered over a period of six months. Half the interviews occurred three months after the death, the other half nine months after the death. In this way it was hoped to avoid seasonal fluctuations in the age and causes of death.

Organisationally, staggered interviewing is inconvenient and lengthens the study period. By preference we wanted to do all our interviewing for the 1987 study in a single period at a single fixed interval since death. Seasonal variations in the death rate would also mean that comparisons between areas would be less valid if each area had a different month's deaths. The issue, then, was whether there existed any grounds to believe that choosing the whole sample from one month would destroy the comparability with the earlier study. The interval since death, and seasonal variation in the age and cause of death were potential sources of bias that required examination.

A literature review had revealed no study except the 1969 'Life before death' study reporting the effect of interval since death on responses or response rates. In the 1969 study it was found that refusals were more common three months after the death, but nine months after it was more difficult to find a suitable respondent. Overall response rates in the two groups were similar. A theoretical worry arose from Colin Murray Parkes' work (chiefly Parkes 1972), which suggested that bereaved people pass through stages in their reaction to loss (for example, numbness and shock, denial, anger and acceptance). Clearly if we were to interview people at a stage when most were passing through a phase of anger, this could affect response rates and bias answers to questions. However, no data were presented by Parkes to support the idea that such patterns follow a fixed time scale. The other possibility to consider was that as time went by people would forget things, so a long interval between death and interview would be inadvisable. Again, no data were available in the literature to test this, apart from a few analyses in an appendix to the 1969 study. It was reported in this appendix that 'the number and extent of the differences were small' between those answering at three and those answering at nine months after the death. For the most part inadequate or 'uncertain' answers were given no more frequently for respondents at nine months than ones approached at three months, although none of those interviewed at three months were dissatisfied with the site of death and fewer were uncertain about this. Recall of basic facts that could be compared with information on the death registration form was similar at the two intervals.

Punched cards containing data still existed from the 1969 study, so that further comparisons of responses at three and nine months were possible. These cards had survived the past twenty years in spite of a serious flood in the building where they were housed. They were re-analysed using a card-sorting machine, a relic from pre-computer days still kept at the Institute. To the accompaniment of a cacophony of machine noises, the cards were sent trundling through the machine to fall into their allotted piles.

To test the idea that those respondents going through a phase of anger might answer differently, questions concerning satisfaction with services were compared. No significant differences were found although the emotional and ethical issues involved in approaching bereaved people shortly after a death were not to be overlooked. In fact, Parkes (1972) presents evidence (page 239) that in widows interviewed at intervals between one and thirteen months after the death, tearfulness during the interview declined a great deal between one and three months. On these grounds, then, three months seemed a reasonable interval. We would be running less risk of upsetting people unduly, and of them forgetting details. The Office of Population Censuses and Surveys (OPCS) guaranteed to supply the death certificates within a month from the end of the registration period selected (in fact they arrived two weeks after the end of the period).

To fit in with this timetable deaths registered in March were chosen for the pilot although we recognised that for the main study we would need to look at seasonal variations in the number and type of deaths before deciding which month or months to cover.

Since 1969 computers have come to play an increasing role in the storage and retrieval systems of the Office of Population Censuses and Surveys. No doubt this represented a significant advantage for OPCS. For us, however, it created difficulties since the coding system used to store information meant that deaths by place of residence in registration districts could not be retrieved; the place of registration (regardless of where the deceased had lived) was the only method of selection available if registration districts were used. We decided to go ahead on this basis and see what difference it made to the sampling.

Before we chose our pilot areas we thought it sensible to select the sample for the main study, as the pilot areas should not be those chosen for the main study. To do this involved a major exercise locating hospices within registration districts, since we wished to stratify the areas by the presence or absence of services so as to ensure that our random sample of areas contained representative numbers of hospice services. Only if this was done would it be at all possible to assess the impact of hospice services on care before death.

St Christopher's Hospice produce an annual directory of hospice services, which are defined as follows:

Hospice is now an internationally accepted term referring to care by a multi-disciplinary team for patients and families facing advanced cancer or other mortal illness. Experienced symptom control and understanding of the support needed for patients and families to find their own strength is backed by teaching and appropriate research. A hospice group aims to give continuity of care in the patients' homes or within a general hospital or they may have specially planned units, often with outpatient clinics and/or day centres. This complementary local service is offered in an area of proven need, integrated with the NHS hospitals and community teams who will refer those patients who need its specialised skills.

Registration districts were combined when necessary to give approximately 1,200 deaths in a year. They were then stratified into three groups:

1 Those with no hospice services.
2 Those with some hospice service (home care, day care or symptom control) but no beds.
3 Those with hospice beds.

In the first two groups registration districts were further stratified into those in metropolitan counties and others, and within these groups they were listed by county alphabetically. The third group was stratified by the number of hospice beds per 1,000 deaths: this ranged from 0.8 to 26.5.

Deaths in the registration districts during the twelve months October 1985 – September 1986 were then summed cumulatively. The numbers were:

		%
In districts with no hospice services	177,626	32
In districts with some hospice service but no beds	123,865	22
In districts with some hospice beds	252,545	46
Total	554,036	100

Twelve areas were chosen by calculating a sampling interval (the total number of deaths divided by twelve) and selecting a starting point from a table of random numbers. The twelve areas thus selected, we were able to proceed with the selection of two areas for the pilot: Epping with no hospice services and Oxford with 14.0 hospice beds per 1,000 deaths. The areas were chosen largely because we knew of trained interviewers who lived in these places.

The 1969 study achieved a response rate of 82% for the main questionnaire to relatives and others who knew the people who died. The pilot to the 1987 study produced a response of 56% of 80 deaths. The main reason for this disturbing difference was that for 15% of the pilot deaths no contact was made with anyone who knew the deceased, and this was directly related to the sampling strategy. Choosing deaths according to their place of registration meant that substantial numbers of people were chosen who lived a long way from the district. Since most people, these days, die in hospital (OPCS 1987), this means that registration districts in small towns or cities surrounded by large areas of countryside (like Oxford) will have a large proportion of people coming in to the city hospitals from far away, dying in them, and the deaths being registered in the city. These people often lived too far away for repeated visits to establish who knew them best and would be willing to act as respondent. Varying the approach to such people – by telephoning or writing – would be fraught with practical problems and could introduce bias into the response.

We concluded that a different sampling approach, based on place of residence, would have to be used for the main study. How we did this is covered in the next chapter.

The questionnaire

The questionnaire to relatives and others who knew the people who died ('the main questionnaire') was complex, with a large number of conditional skips to cover the wide variety of circumstances in which people die. It was designed with several points in mind: first, there was a need to ask some of the same questions as in the 1969 survey, so that comparisons could be made. Important items, such as the presence or absence of symptoms, services received and information given by doctors were retained for this purpose. However, this had to be traded against the need to find better ways of asking some questions, and to deal with new topics in response to the changed pattern of services since 1969.

A number of developments in the measurement of symptoms and of disability had taken place since 1969. For example, the production of composite measures of 'Activities of daily living' to measure levels of restriction had reached the status of a small industry. One or two scales, we felt, deserved consideration, in particular that of Mahoney and Barthel (1965) which is used widely as a measure of need for nursing care as well as disability (see Seale 1987 for a review of such measures in stroke rehabilitation research). However, experiments with this scale led us to conclude that its use in a questionnaire such as ours would involve substantial and time consuming probing of subsidiary questions for each activity. It would also mean that we would lose comparability with the 1969 survey.

In the area of measurement of symptoms a number of other scales – again largely American – had also been unearthed during the literature review. Melzack (1975) had constructed an index of pain used in the National Hospice Study (1986) and also one for nausea (1985). Snaith in Leeds had constructed an anxiety and depression scale (1976). Spitzer's quality of life index (Spitzer et al 1981) was used widely in hospice research (see, for example, the National Hospice Study 1986, Ward 1985). The problem with all of these scales for our purposes was that they required extensive questioning about each symptom, and some were designed for use with the patient, or by the interviewer observing the patient – clearly impossible given our study design. Their inclusion would also mean that comparability with the 1969 study would be lost. As a result, we decided not to use any of these 'ready made' scales.

A further consideration in our redesign of the questionnaire was our desire to explore the institutional care of the dying to a greater extent than last time, and home care less so. To this end the new questionnaire cut out a lot of detail asked in 1969 on services received at the home, and added a number of items on the quality of care and symptom control in hospices, hospitals and other institutions. A new section on day care was added to reflect the increased provision of this facility for the terminally ill since 1969 (see Seale 1989). We also included an extra section on nursing and old peoples' homes and a short sequence on outpatient attendance. The aim throughout was to gain estimates of the numbers receiving these services, to describe the experience of them, and to assess their quality. A recurrent concern was to ensure that the principles espoused by hospice practitioners (for example, Saunders 1978) were covered. Thus we wanted to know whether relatives and friends had themselves been made to feel welcome by staff, and whether they had taken part in the care of the people who were dying. Symptom relief, particularly pain relief, is an area in which hospice practitioners claim special expertise, so a number of questions were asked about this. We also collected information about medical procedures and their purpose in order to establish whether palliative care rather than a more 'aggressive', curative approach was being applied.

Questionnaires for doctors and nurses attending the patients in the last twelve months of life were also designed, and similar principles applied here. The 1969 study had involved interviews with a range of people providing domiciliary services – including home help organisers as well as district nurses, health visitors and general practitioners. In keeping with the intention to focus more on institutional care, it was decided to approach domiciliary nurses and general practitioners but not home help organisers in the 1987 study. The pilot of the 1969 study had shown that general practitioners could not be relied on to recall the circumstances of individual patients who had died some months previously, as notes were often not available any more. General practitioners would therefore be sent a postal questionnaire asking only for their general views about services in their local area, and would not be asked to recall individual patients. Hospital consultants would be asked for their views both about services in general and for accounts of particular patients. To this end, questionnaires were designed with items covering inpatient experiences – details of medical procedures, their purpose and assessments of their effectiveness, as well as other areas of hospital care. Many of the questions to professionals were designed so that direct comparisons with the views of, and information provided by, relatives could be made. Thus, for example, consultants were asked the same questions as relatives about symptom control in the patients they looked after.

Professionals

An important purpose of the pilot study was to test how easily we could identify the specific doctors and nurses who saw the patient from information gained in the main questionnaire. Identifying general practitioners proved to be relatively straightforward, as the vast majority of people were able to give us a name and address of the relevant doctor. Any inaccuracies in the information were checked by us using the Medical Directory (Longman Group Ltd 1985) although we asked interviewers on the main study to check the information themselves in locally available lists, so as to improve accuracy still further.

Identifying domiciliary nurses on the pilot proved deceptively easy. Of the 45 patients for whom main interviews were completed, 12 were visited by domiciliary nurses, involving 15 different nurses. Four of these were private nurses, care attendants or voluntary workers. For the remaining eleven, who were district nurses, it was a relatively simple matter to write to the district nursing officers with the names of the patients, who then wrote back with details of the nurses concerned. This experience lulled us into a false sense of security; in retrospect it is clear that our choice of pilot areas had been ones for which community nursing service records had been particularly good, and nursing officers particularly helpful.

Identifying the hospital consultants proved much more difficult, and our approach to them led to events which were to delay the start of the main study.

In the first place, few respondents could be relied upon to recall the name of the consultant under whom the patient was admitted. Where names were given, these were often inaccurate. This meant that we needed to write to the managers of the hospitals and hospices concerned, with lists of names of patients known to have been inpatients. In Epping, after lost letters which had to be sent again and numerous follow-up telephone calls, the information was provided by the hospital managers within two months. In Oxford, where three hospitals were involved, two managers wrote to say that they could not release the information without the approval of the Central Oxford Research Ethics Committee (COREC). The other did not reply.

Negotiations with COREC were lengthy and at times frustrating. By the time permission to ask for the information was received in October 1987, the Epping half of the pilot had been completed. The ethical and practical issues involved in approaching ethical committees about a study of this nature will be discussed in chapter four. Interviewing Epping consultants did produce one doctor who enquired whether the ethical committee had approved the study, but the difference in the readiness of managers in the two areas to release information to us is of interest. Clearly ethical standards were not consistent from one district to another. Our experience of the main study was to demonstrate immense variability in this respect.

The Central Oxford Research Ethics Committee began by sending us a nine page form with nine further pages of instructions. The form was clearly designed for use with proposals for clinical trials as it asked about samples that were to be taken from patients, substances to be administered and other invasive and non invasive tests. It made no provision for health care professionals to be the subjects of study. It also asked for 17 copies of our questionnaires. Since we had six questionnaires this would have involved sending the committee 102 questionnaires, 17 of which would have been 29 pages long. For some of the questionnaires this would have involved producing more copies for the committee than were needed for the pilot study!

A letter pointing out these problems received the concession that only two copies of each questionnaire need be submitted, but the form should still be completed. This was duly done.

A month later, COREC replied as follows:

The application was considered at some length at the recent meeting of COREC and we still had some reservations about the study methods (rather than the aims of the study which seem admirable), particularly in relation to the interviews with relatives and community nursing staff. The direct approach to relatives/friends was viewed with concern and normally, in studies of this nature COREC would consider that an approach of this nature should only be made after discussion with the relevant GP. Although it was recognised that the information on death and causes was a matter of public record, COREC wished to reassure itself that any additional information or comment obtained from either relatives or professionals was obtained in the most correct manner. We have asked for the comments of the community nurses on this point before a final decision is made by the Committee.

Our reply pointed out, amongst other things, that the community nurse managers had already supplied us with the names of the nurses concerned, so could have had no ethical objections to the study. Nor could we have identified general practitioners of the sample before we did our main interviews. The committee had also not recognised that we had already completed interviews with relatives and were seeking ethical approval only for our approach to doctors and nurses.

One of us (AC) attended the COREC meeting three weeks later. These are her notes on the meeting:

The main issue they wanted to discuss was our approach to relatives. The points raised were:
1 *What information were relatives given?* I referred them to the leaflet we left with the people we saw. This was the one document we sent them when they first contacted us and we wrote explaining that their form did not seem to apply to us as we were not seeing patients, volunteers or controls. They appeared to have lost it. I gave them another copy which was passed round. No comments were made on the leaflet.

2 *How much time were relatives given to decide whether to participate?*
I said that we explained that we would like to talk to the person
who could tell us most about the subject's last year of life. When
we'd identified that person we asked if they were willing to help
and if they agreed the interviewer either went ahead or made
arrangements to come back later.

3 *Would it not be better to write in advance?* This would be difficult
as we did not know who to write to, and might create more anxieties than a face to face contact, in which the interviewer could respond to queries.

4 *They thought it would be better to contact the general practitioner
first.* I said that I thought people had a right to make up their own
minds whether or not to answer our questions or not. They said
that they were not suggesting general practitioners should stop
them but they could indentify people who might be upset and
facilitate the study. (We did not pursue this). I asked whether they
were talking about the general practitioner of the relative or the
person who died? This was not answered. I pointed out that we
could not identify the general practitioner of either. They said they
could do this from their hospital records. I pointed out that not
everyone died in hospital. They said this could be done from other
records. I tried to explain that this was likely to be an unsatis-
factory process from the researcher's point of view.

5 *One member said he had been upset after bereavement* by people
calling and asking him questions and had not felt strong enough to
refuse them. I asked what sort of people. He said undertakers and
florists. I pointed out that these were commercial people. Another
member said that as we were going to write a book about the study
we were commercial. I disagreed. I should also have pointed out
that there was an interval of months between the death and our
approach whereas undertakers and florists contact people within
days and that the royalties from Institute books do not go to the
authors but to the Institute – a registered charity.

6 Another member said that our results were likely to be biased
because of the people who did not participate. I said we were likely
to have a bigger non-response bias if we went through doctors first.
I could have asked what this had to do with ethics.

7 The chairman said that they were concerned that we had interviewed the relatives without going to the ethical committee first or
getting in touch with the general practitioners. I pointed out that
the MRC guidelines said that an approach to doctors was not

necessary when interviewing people indentified from public records, but that the Local Medical Committee should be informed. We had done this before we started interviewing relatives.

8 The chairman said he had spoken to the MRC about the study. He was surprised the MRC had not insisted on us getting the approval of all the ethics committees before agreeing to fund the project. I pointed out that selecting areas took time and the basis on which we were planning to select the areas for the main study had changed as a result of our experiences on the pilot inquiry – from areas in which the deaths occurred to areas in which the people who died were normally resident.

9 The Committee had no objection about our approaching doctors – it was up to them to decide whether to respond or not. The Chairman thanked me for coming and said they would write and let me know their decision.

Committee members have not been identified individually in these notes as they were not introduced to me.

After this we received a letter on the 13th October 1987, giving permission for the second half of the pilot to proceed:

Thank you very much for coming to our meeting last week to explain the methods used in your study. We are sorry if any inconvenience was caused. COREC did feel that the aims of the study were admirable but nevertheless, it had some concerns about the methods used in approaching the bereaved. Whilst COREC was unhappy about the first part of the study, which had been completed, it gave approval in principle for the remaining portion, which appeared to raise fewer ethical problems. COREC felt that if you wished to undertake further studies in this area (Oxford) it would be willing to assist you, particularly in identifying channels of approach to subjects. COREC felt in addition it should notify the MRC of its concerns of funding projects which have not had ethics committee clearance.

We wish you every success with your study.

After all this we were then in a position, after some three months delay, to write again to the Oxford hospital managers for the names of consultants under whom the patients in the sample had been admitted. This was a straightforward matter in the case of one of the three hospitals, but in the case of the other two, the managers insisted on getting the consultants' permission before forwarding their names to us. Thus mini-surveys of consultants were begun, before we could have their permission to do our survey! Consultants being consultants, most did not reply, and after many phone calls we obtained the names of a few. By mid-December, six months after first writing to the hospital managers, we had sufficient information to send questionnaires and seek interviews with consultants in Oxford.

Response rates for the domiciliary nurses in the pilot were encouraging (seven out of ten general questionnaires, eleven out of eleven specific patient questionnaires), but for the consultants less so (nine out of 19 general questionnaires – 47% – and 14 out of 34 specific patient questionnaires – 41%). It was clear that getting information about and from hospital doctors was going to be a struggle. General practitioners, on the other hand, seemed much more willing to complete postal questionnaires about their general views (74% of 35). But for five deaths in the Oxford region we were unable to identify the general practitioner. We wrote to COREC to ask for help with this as members of the committee had stated in the meeting that this was an example of how they could help. However, we received no reply.

Thus the second half of the pilot was valuable in alerting us to the ethical committee issue, and in providing practice in gaining information from hospital bureaucracies. It failed to alert us to the difficulties we would have in getting information from district nursing officers, but it gave us a good idea of potential response rates from the professionals concerned once they were identified. Certain matters of question wording were also improved, and the comments of one hospice doctor in the pilot on our questions concerning the treatment of pain were extremely useful.

Conclusion

The pilot study led us to revise our sampling procedure, and on purely pragmatic, if not ethical, grounds the Oxford experience showed us that we would have to approach all the local ethical committees involved in the main study. Both these areas reflect changes since 1969 when the previous study was done. The computerisation of records in OPCS since that date meant that a sample of deaths of people resident in a registration district could not be drawn up. We had instead to structure the sample according to local authority areas, as this sampling procedure was feasible on OPCS computers (see Chapter 3). In 1969 local ethical committees played very little part in scrutinising research proposals, if such committees existed at all in many areas. Ethical monitoring of research had now expanded and we could not ignore the requirements of these committees. Although COREC had not raised the issue as an ethical consideration, discussion of our plans with the Institute's advisory committee led us to decide to ask relatives' permission for our approach to doctors and nurses if we needed to find out about the medical care of individuals, as we did if the patient had received care from nurses at home, or had hospital care. It was felt that seeking such signed consent for our enquiries was worth the lower response rate that any refusals to give permission might entail, and that having relatives' permission might increase the response rate from doctors and nurses.

The pilot also provided us with valuable experience in recruiting and training interviewers, and in seeing how the questionnaire items worked out in practice. Less tangible matters that are rarely reported in formal accounts of research studies – such as how to persuade local administrators to release names, or how to work oneself past the defensive barriers put up around consultants by their secretaries – were also a part of the many benefits of the pilot exercise.

3 The sample of areas and deaths

The pilot study had shown us that our initial sampling strategy, based on deaths occurring in registration districts, would lead to a high failure rate. We needed to select a sample based on area of residence so that interviewers' time and travel costs would remain within reasonable limits and we would get a good response rate.

Over the years OPCS had selected six samples of births and two of deaths for ISSMC and one of us (AC) had visited Titchfield to meet the people who had done the work. But the person with whom the Institute had had most contact had since retired so we both went down to Titchfield to meet the people who were now involved. It proved a useful as well as an enjoyable visit. We found out that they were planning to develop a computer programme to select a random sample of deaths from the study areas once we had chosen them. This would have taken time and cost quite a lot. When we suggested that we should select the deaths from a list of the registration numbers that they would send us, they were relieved and we had saved time and money.

Choosing the sample areas

We were told by OPCS that if we wanted to select deaths by place of residence we would have to change our sampling areas from registration districts to local authority areas, split into ward districts, if necessary. It could also be about six months after registration before copies of the forms could be made available to us. Since we had little choice in the matter we decided that interviewing would have to be done as soon as possible after receipt of the death registration forms. This would mean that Parkes' idea that six months was a time when people would not wish to talk about the experience would be violated. On balance we decided that this was acceptable, as Parkes had provided no systematic evidence to support his idea. We suspected, too, that emotional reactions to bereavement were unlikely to run to a strict timetable.

The initial research proposal stated that ten areas would be selected for the study, with 80 deaths taken from each one to make a sample of 800. On reflection we felt it would be better to take a slightly larger number of areas, twelve, and to take 70 deaths in each area making a total sample size of 840. It was important to have in our sample enough hospice deaths to make comparisons with other deaths feasible. On the basis of the estimates of other authors (Lunt, personal communication; Fry 1983; Wilkes 1986) we reckoned that between three and five per cent of our 840 deaths would occur in hospices (yielding between 24 and 40 hospice deaths). After discussion with the Institute's advisory committee which approved the strategy we decided to take an additional random sample in areas where there were hospices, and select deaths which happened in hospices, so creating an extra group of hospice deaths. This extra sample would be taken from the month following that in which the random sample was registered.

The next step was to group all the local authority areas in England so that each area would have the minimum number of deaths in a year to make a sample of 70 in any one month feasible. Some areas with large populations were split into two or three sub-areas according to ward boundaries, as death statistics by ward were available from OPCS on computer print-out. In order to do this in a way that would produce areas made up of adjoining wards in every case, maps showing the location of electoral wards had to be consulted. Maps relating to the 1981 Census were held in the OPCS library at St Catherine's House, London. For the most part these sufficed, but in some cases there had been boundary changes between 1981 and 1986 (the year for which we had statistics on numbers of deaths by electoral ward). No maps were available for these areas at the library, and extensive enquiries revealed that the only practical way of getting these maps was to telephone the local town halls. In some instances payment was requested, in others maps were free. In a few, maps were not available and local street indexes were obtained from which ward boundaries could be estimated.

The end result of this exercise was that 309 areas were listed. These were made up from an original list of 411 local authorities. In 93 instances our areas were made up from combined local authorities with sparse populations, and in 31 they were made up from sub groups of wards in very populous local authorities.

We were particularly anxious that our sample of twelve areas should be representative of those with and without hospice services. We also wanted the sample to have the appropriate proportion of metropolitan and county areas, and to have a balanced geographical spread. The last two conditions were relatively easy, since local authorities were already listed according to whether they were metropolitan or county, and geographical location was simply a matter of using a country map. Locating hospice services presented somewhat more of a problem. We had a 1987 directory from St Christopher's (St Christopher's Hospice 1987) and both inpatient units, along with their bed numbers, and other hospice services, such as home care, were listed. Addresses were given, and for the most part postcodes.

Many of the hospice services could be placed in one of our areas by place names, or with the aid of an ordinary map of England. Thus in Warrington local authority a hospice called Saint Rocco's was listed, located in the town of Warrington. In populous areas, where we had split the local authority into ward groups, things were more difficult. Birmingham, for example, had been split into five areas and two inpatient units had to be located. Sometimes ward names were a part of the hospice address. In cases of doubt we consulted a microfiche supplied by OPCS which listed postcodes according to their ward. Of course, postcodes for the hospices were not always listed, so telephone calls to the hospices themselves were sometimes made.

The areas were listed by the three factors in the following way: first, three categories of hospice service were distinguished – no services, home service only, and inpatient service. The areas with inpatient hospice services were listed in ascending order according to the number of beds per 1000 deaths and that was the only stratification used for that group. The other two groups were divided first into metropolitan and county areas and within these four groups areas were listed on a north to south basis. To some extent locating hospices in the areas was an artificial exercise, as the catchment areas which the hospices served would not have been coterminous with the area boundaries. Thus in Birmingham, the three areas listed as being without hospices would probably receive the services of the hospices located in the other two Birmingham areas. However, in the absence of information about catchment policies (Lunt showed these to be very variable in hospices, if they existed at all – Lunt 1981), we felt the method we used represented a rough and ready approach to ensuring a reasonable spread of hospice services in our areas.

Having arranged the areas according to the three factors by which we wanted to stratify the selection, the numbers of deaths in 1986 were summed cumulatively. A sampling interval was calculated by dividing the total number of deaths by twelve. A randomly selected number below the sampling interval was taken as a starting point and the area with that number of deaths within the cumulative total was selected. Adding the sampling interval repeatedly resulted in the selection of eleven more areas. This procedure ensures that areas are selected with a probability proportional to the number of deaths within them. The twelve areas thus chosen are shown in Table 1.

Health authority areas are not always coterminous with local authority areas and this fact, together with the effect of combining areas, meant that our twelve areas were covered by 19 health authorities. An account of our negotiations with ethical committees will be given in the next chapter, but suffice to say that Kirklees and Leominster/ Wyre Forest were eventually dropped from the sample, largely because of refusals by ethical committees. Our decision to select twelve rather than ten areas was fortunate.

Table 1 Twelve study areas for 'Life before death in 1987'

Area	Local authority or part of local authority	Type	Number of deaths in 1986	Hospice services	Health authority
1	Hyndburn Rossendale	County	1927	None	(1) Blackburn, Hyndburn and Ribble Valley (2) Burnley, Pendle and Rossendale (3) Rochdale
2	Leominster Wyre Forest	County	1560	None	(1) Herefordshire (2) Kidderminster and district
3	Hart Rushmoor	County	1232	None	(1) Basingstoke and North Hampshire (2) West Surrey and N.E. Hampshire
4	Kirklees (West)	Met.	2313	None	Huddersfield
5	Birmingham (Central)	Met.	2483	None	(1) West Birmingham (2) Central Birmingham (3) East Birmingham
6	Kingston upon Hull	County	3055	Home care	Hull
7	Luton	County	1481	Home care	South Bedfordshire
8	Rochdale	Met.	2436	Home care	Rochdale
9	Bromley (East)	Met.	1779	Home care	Bromley
10	Lewes	County	1193	6.7*	Brighton
11	Lambeth	Met.	2668	11.6*	(1) West Lambeth (2) Camberwell
12	Bradford (North)	Met.	2712	19.2*	(1) Airedale (2) Bradford

* Hospice beds per 1,000 deaths.

The sample of deaths

It was evident from published statistics that the variation in the number of adult deaths occurring in different months of the year was considerable. In 1985, deaths in January were 25% higher than the average for the year, deaths in September 14% lower. In 1984, the increase in the early months was not quite so great, but again January and March had the highest numbers and September the lowest. Months that were nearest to the average were November and April or May. The figures showing this are in Table 2.

Table 2 Variation in number of adult deaths by months of the year

| | 1984 | | 1985 | |
	Number	Variation from mean	Number	Variation from mean
January	53,338	+ 15%	60,565	+ 25%
February	48,608	+ 5%	53,336	+ 10%
March	53,098	+ 14%	58,749	+ 21%
April	50,037	+ 8%	48,920	+ 1%
May	46,905	+ 1%	45,748	− 5%
June	42,220	− 9%	42,890	− 11%
July	41,840	− 10%	42,453	− 12%
August	40,333	− 13%	42,055	− 13%
September	41,081	− 12%	41,418	− 14%
October	45,043	− 3%	44,080	− 9%
November	45,081	− 3%	49,116	+ 2%
December	50,209	+ 8%	51,330	+ 6%
Total number of deaths	557,793	—	580,660	—

Source: OPCS 1986, 1987

However, within each month the proportions of deaths occurring to people of different age groups did not show such a big difference: the proportion occurring to people aged 85 or more varied in 1984 between 17.9% (July and September) and 20.1% (April) and in 1985 between 18.5% (July) and 21.6% (March) (see Table 3). The broad cause of death showing the greatest seasonal variation were respiratory diseases: these accounted for 9.1% of all deaths in 1984 (8.0% in September, 11.9% in April) and 11% in 1985 (8.3% in August and September, 14.6% in March). November, May, October and April are the months in which the numbers of deaths and their distributions by age and cause seem closest to the average for the year.

In the event, the study was done largely with registrations from October, with some from November. Although November would have been the better month according to the previous observations, we were concerned that using that month for our main sample would mean that we would be seeking interviews close to the summer holiday period.

Table 3 Proportion of deaths to people aged 85 or more and proportion attributed to respiratory disease by month of year

	Proportion of adult deaths of people aged 85 or more		Proportion of all deaths attributable to respiratory disease	
	1984	*1985*	*1984*	*1985*
January	20.0%	21.2%	11.5%	13.2%
February	19.4%	21.5%	10.9%	13.7%
March	20.0%	21.6%	11.7%	14.6%
April	20.1%	20.5%	11.9%	11.8%
May	18.6%	19.1%	9.9%	9.8%
June	18.0%	18.9%	9.0%	9.4%
July	17.9%	18.5%	8.6%	8.6%
August	18.0%	18.7%	8.4%	8.3%
September	17.9%	18.3%	8.0%	8.3%
October	18.5%	19.1%	9.2%	8.9%
November	18.8%	19.7%	9.4%	10.0%
December	19.5%	20.6%	10.4	11.7%
All year	19.0%	19.9%	9.1%	11.0%
Total number of deaths	557,793	580,660	566,233	589,259

Source: OPCS 1986,1987

When it became clear that our sample of areas was to be reduced to ten and therefore 700 deaths, we decided to select an extra ten deaths in the remaining ten areas. Our original 700 deaths were randomly selected from listings of deaths of people aged 15 and over registered in October 1987. Listings of November deaths were also produced for us by OPCS and a further 700 deaths were selected from these. From the November deaths, ten in each area were added to the October random sample making the total sample size of the random sample 800.

Within this 800 were 30 deaths in hospices (3.8%), which was roughly as expected given the estimates of between three and five per cent given by other authors (see earlier). We thought that selecting the hospice deaths from the remaining 600 November deaths might produce another 20-30 hospice deaths but in fact it only produced eleven, making a total of 41 hospice deaths in the sample.

The difference in the proportions of deaths in hospices in the two samples, 3.8% and 1.8% is a cause for some concern. We checked the death registration forms to see if we had overlooked any in the second sample but no more were found. And it will be shown later, in chapter 9, that there was complete agreement betweeen the information from the death registration form and that obtained at the interviews on whether or not the deaths occurred in a hospice. The discrepancy means that our estimate of the proportion of deaths occurring in hospices is reduced from 3.8% in the initial sample to 2.9% in the larger one.

Interviewing was done as soon as possible after receiving the death registration forms from OPCS. Naturally, there was a delay while address lists for each interviewer were compiled. The eventual intervals between the deaths and the interviews are shown in Table 4. In practice, most of the interviewing was done between six and eight months after the deaths had occurred. The deaths for which the interval was more than nine months were usually coroners' cases whose registration had been delayed pending an inquest.

Table 4 Interval between death and interview

Number of months	Number	%
5	3	0.5
6	187	29.3
7	259	40.7
8	141	22.1
9	26	4.1
10	8	1.3
11	3	0.5
12	6	0.9
13	4	0.6
Total number of interviews (including extra hospice deaths) [= 100%]	637*	

* For nine interviews the date was not recorded.

Stratifying by the geographical location of hospice services produced no obvious association between the presence of a unit or home care service and the number of hospice deaths. Twenty eight of the 41 hospice deaths eventually selected were in areas where no inpatient unit was located. In fact, ten of these deaths were in a hospice located just outside the Hart and Rushmoor area, but whose catchment area clearly included Hart and Rushmoor. A further seven were in Birmingham where we happened to select an area of the city where the hospices serving the city were not located. Six out of twelve (50%) of our areas were counties, which compares with 62% of deaths in the population which occur to residents in county areas. There was a reasonable north to south distribution but a cluster of areas located around Manchester.

Conclusion

The sampling exercise, then, represented our best efforts to create a study that would first be based on a random sample of adult deaths, would second enable valid comparisons to be made with the 1969 study, and third give a representative proportion of people who had received hospice services. The chief difficulties in achieving these aims arose from the limitations of the OPCS retrieval system which imposed a delay of six months before interviews could be done and in the variable criteria of local ethical committees which meant that two of the selected areas had to be dropped. Our attempt to select extra deaths in hospices produced fewer than we had hoped. We turn now to the story of our negotiations with ethical committees.

4 Ethical committees

As a result of our pilot study and our contacts with the Central Oxford Research Ethics Committee we had to face up to the fact that the MRC who were funding our study held different views from us about the circumstances in which the approval of ethical committees should be sought. Our experiences also made us clarify and record our views and discuss them with our advisory committee. But initially it was not clear that our position was at odds with that of the MRC.

Sequence of events

When the study was funded we were sent a copy of a statement by the MRC, 'Responsibility in the use of personal medical information for research: principles and guide to practice' (1985). After reading this we wrote to the MRC in February 1987:

> As the sample for our new study of *Life before death* is identified from death certificates, not from medical records, our study does not require the consent of the doctor or of any other local body (para. 2.1.4 iii), but it would seem sensible to notify the local medical committee beforehand, particularly as we will subsequently be approaching general practitioners and hospital consultants and sisters. We thought that when we wrote to the local medical committees we should explain that the MRC was funding the study and that this funding indicated that our plans conformed to the guidelines of the MRC Standing Committee on the Use of Medical Information for Research – the relevant body for national studies (See para. 1.3.1). I would be grateful if you would confirm that this is so.

The paragraphs we referred to were:

2.1.4 (iii) Surveys of the apparently well population
Surveys may be made of 'total' populations or of 'samples' selected from public records, such as the electoral roll. A direct approach (e.g. by postal questionnaire or visit/interview) to members of the public selected in this way does not require consent of the doctor or of any local medical body. Nevertheless, it is sensible to notify

the local general practitioners and local medical committee before-hand when carrying out a survey in an area. In population surveys it should be sufficient to obtain the consent of the individual to simple investigative procedures. Care should be taken to respect the confidentiality of information obtained from members of the public who may not necessarily wish the information to be passed to the general practitioner. The right of people to elect not to take part in surveys must be respected and an unreasonable number of repeat invitations avoided.

1.3.1 Ethical committee approval

Local ethical committee approval is required for research that in-volves people, whether or not they are patients in the context of the study. If it is not considered reasonably practicable or it is inadvis-able to seek their consent, the ethical committee should be informed of this in the research protocol. Advice on the composi-tion of an ethical committee has been given by the Royal College of Physicians. For national studies, a view should be sought from the BMA Central Ethical Committee or from the MRC Standing Com-mittee on the Use of Medical Information for Research.

The reply from the MRC was:

I am afraid that it is not possible for us to give an assurance that MRC funding of this study indicates that your plans conform to the guidelines of the MRC Standing Committee on the Use of Medical Information for Research. However, it would be appro-priate for you to tell the local medical committee that the MRC expects grantholders to follow our guidelines and that you intend to do so. If after having considered further your procedures in rela-tion to the guidelines, you need further clarification of any points, please do not hesitate to contact me again.

In July 1987 we sent a letter to various officials in our two pilot areas telling them about the study and incorporating the suggestion from the MRC. The people we wrote to were the secretaries of local medi-cal committees (representing general practitioners) and, in Oxford, to the Secretary of the Medical Executive Committee at the Oxford-shire Health Authority (who turned out to also be the Secretary of COREC – the Central Oxford Research Ethics Committee) and in Epping to the Chairman of the District Consultant Committee. We had consulted various members of our advisory committee about this approach and received a range of advice about seeking the approval of local ethical committees or 'avoiding them like the plague'.

In the event, the people in Oxford got in touch with the MRC and they in turn wrote to say that 'the Council must insist on your obtaining ethical committee approval to cover all those areas within which you propose to study'.

We decided to do this on pragmatic grounds: we needed MRC funds and we wanted as good a response as possible from the doctors and other professionals we approached in our study. But we did not agree on ethical grounds. We put our views in a draft paper which we discussed with our advisory committee in November 1987. The relevant parts of that paper and the discussion are presented next.

The ISSMC and ethical committees

Principles We think that ethical committees should protect patients in relation to:

1 The confidentiality of their medical records (including the diagnosis).
2 The use of invasive procedures for research.

We do *not* think it is appropriate for ethical committees to concern themselves with surveys of people identified from public records. They are not the custodians of people's civil rights. People do not belong to their doctors and there should be no interference with people's liberty to make up their own minds about what questions they should answer and in what circumstances.

Implications These principles have implications for ISSMC's work in relation to surveys in which information from medical records is sought – but not access to those records, and the practicality of doing certain studies on a national basis.

Surveys in which information from medical records is sought but not access to those records. This was the situation in our study of *Elderly people, their medicines and their doctors* (Cartwright and Smith 1988). The elderly people were identified by a postal screen of a sample taken from the electoral register. They were then interviewed and towards the end of the interview were asked if they were willing for their doctors to give us information about their health and treatment. Those who agreed were asked to sign a form giving their consent and a copy of this was given to the doctors when we asked them for information about the medicines they had prescribed for particular patients. The approval of ethical committees was not sought. The situation in our study of *Life before death* is rather similar, except that the 'patient' is dead.

The practicality of doing national studies which need ethical approval. While there is no national organisation from which ethical approval for national studies can be sought, it is probably inappropriate for us to take on national studies which need this approval – although we will still try to do our new Life before death one. But if we had been asked to obtain this approval before the MRC funded the study (as they say is now their policy) this would have made it quite impractical because so much work is involved in designing the sampling frame and identifying the study areas. And on that study we changed our sampling frame as a result of our pilot experience. In addition, ethical committees generally ask to see copies of questionnaires. To have designed and typed the seven questionnaires we used on the pilot study before we obtained funding would have been impossible.

Views of ISSMC's Advisory Committee

During the discussion of this paper, members made a number of points:

1 Ethical committees only exist within the NHS; there is no similar mechanism within, say, the social services.
2 It is not appropriate for organisations to demand ethical committee approval for surveys of people identified from public records – even if they are asked questions about their health and use of services. For example, OPCS does not seek such approval for its health questions on the General Household Survey.
3 ISSMC tends to do studies of people identified from public records, but also of the health professionals such people identify. It is this dual approach which has recently led to some of its studies being brought to the attention of ethical committees.
4 As long as there is no national body that can give ethical approval, doing national studies in several areas involves long negotiations and delays if approval has to be sought in each area. Although there might be some knock on effect from one committee to another, this by no means always happens.
5 The reasons for referring studies to ethical committees were often political rather than ethical.

6 Ethical committees often concern themselves with scientific rather than ethical issues. If a research proposal aimed to do things that it could not do in practice, this was unethical. However, funding bodies, such as the MRC, refer studies to appropriate scientific experts. Ethical committees seldom, if ever, use outside experts. If people are to be protected against poor research, ethical committees are not the appropriate organisation.

7 Clinical ethical committees are not satisfactory bodies to make decisions about psychological and other social science research. Some university departments are lobbying for local committees to be set up to deal with this.

8 It was reported that some surveys were being described as 'statistics collection' or 'management studies' to avoid the label of research and the consequent referral to an ethics committee.

With these and one or two other provisos not relevant to this study the advisory committee endorsed the draft statement.

They also made two practical suggestions for the main study of Life before death. The first was that we should try to obtain the support of the BMA Central Ethical Committee for the study. If we could do this it would be likely to facilitate approval of the local committees. The second was that we should ask the relatives we interviewed whether they would have any objection to the doctors and nurses of the deceased giving us information about the person's illness and treatment. This might allay anxieties among some ethical committee members and improve the response of the professionals. Both these suggestions were adopted.

Approach to ethical committees

The Chairman of the BMA Central Ethical Committee responded swiftly to our request for advice about ways in which his committee might facilitate us getting approval for the study from local ethical committees. Within a week he wrote in November 1987 to explain that the committee 'cannot presume formally to give ethical approval.' However, he went on to say: 'It may however help you if, when you seek ethical approval from local committees, you indicate that this proposal has Central Ethical Committee support. I am happy to assure you of that support.' He added that his committee advised 'researchers involved in multicentre trials that they might invite one local committee to give approval and subsequently invite others to agree to accept the adjudication of the first.'

We used this last strategy to some extent but as it was clearly going to take some time to get the approval of any local ethical committee and as we were anxious to get on with the study we wrote to most of them just before Christmas 1987. We sent an outline of the study and a leaflet about this Institute with a covering letter:

I am writing to you in your capacity as Chairman of your research Ethics Committee to seek your approval of a study we are planning.

In 1969 this Institute did a study, subsequently published by Routledge and Kegan Paul as a book *Life before death*, which described the last twelve months in the lives of a random sample of adults who had died recently. We now have a grant from the Medical Research Council to do a similar study of people dying in October 1987.

As in the previous project, the study will be a national one in twelve randomly selected areas. One of those that has been chosen is (name of area).

The study has the support of the BMA Central Ethical Committee. In order to obtain funding by the MRC its methods were endorsed by scientific experts in the relevant field, and the MRC has accepted our assurance that we would follow the ethical guidelines laid down in their statement: 'Responsibility in the use of personal medical information for research.' So we hope your committee will be willing to give the study its approval. Interviewing is scheduled to start at the beginning of April 1988 and it will take some time to organise this, so it would be very helpful if we could have an early response to this request. I would be grateful if, on receipt of this letter, you would let me know how soon we can expect this.

I am enclosing an outline of the project and a leaflet about the Institute. Please let me, or my colleague, Clive Seale, know if you would like any more information.

Response of ethical committees

Of the 19 committees we wrote to we had approval from three by the end of January, from a further twelve by the end of February, and from two more by mid-March. This sounds relatively straightforward but it involved many telephone calls and letters. Some sent forms for us to fill in, others wanted copies of the questionnaire, and one wanted a copy of the book about the earlier study. Some of the questions they raised related to the interviewers, any financial interests of the researchers in the study and possible overlap with other local studies. One wanted copies of our CVs.

Another issue raised was that the study 'could be regarded as an intrusion into grief.' When we received this response we contacted Dr Colin Murray Parkes who wrote to the secretary of that committee:

Re: Ethics Committee Application Life Before Death

I write both as a psychiatrist who has carried out much research in the field of bereavement and as a recent member of our own Ethics Committee here at The London Hospital.

Having read this application carefully I am of the opinion that the project is much more likely to benefit the participants than to harm them. It is my experience that those people who agree to co-operate with a project of this kind find it personally helpful to talk to a person from outside the family about events that are of great concern to them. I have found repeatedly and in several research projects of this kind, that, after talking at length about the last weeks of the life of a person who has died, it is the respondents who are thanking *me* for listening rather than me thanking them for helping with my research.

Any bereaved people who are not ready to talk will decline the invitation to take part and I know that the interviewers will be instructed not to press them.

One of the problems of bereaved people is to bring something worthwhile out of the loss. I believe that most are glad to find that their experiences, however awful, can be of help to others.

Yours sincerely,
Colin M Parkes MD FRCPsych

That committee considered this but still felt they were not able to support the proposal. The other committee 'unable to approve' our research were also concerned with the effects of the research on bereaved relatives. They were sent a copy of Dr Parkes' letter but replied:

. . . there was no evidence in your submission that arrangements had been made to "follow through" or instigate support for the bereaved should your enquiries reveal problems or revive anxieties and distress. Whilst this District has an active bereavement counselling service our resources could not stretch to any additional workload. Compounding the difficult ethical issues were questions of methodology. Your sample selection was such that findings would have reflected the needs of those who had had the opportunity to prepare for the death and those resulting from suddden death – generalising from such findings raises questions of validity.

Apparently this was only the second proposal this committee had ever turned down. The chairman was apologetic and said he had been unable to persuade the lay members to support it. He told us that a survey of elderly people done by a university had led to some people being upset and this had come to the notice of local general practitioners.

We did not receive this last rejection until 16 May (although the committee meeting was on 20 April) and we decided not to pursue the matter further although we thought the comment in the last sentence of their letter could have been refuted. Our study was intended to cover a random sample of adult deaths so could be the basis for certain generalisations, but also it would be possible to analyse different types of deaths separately and avoid inappropriate generalisations.

The two ethical committees who did not approve our studies did so basically because of their anxieties about the possible distress that might be caused by our interviews. Although we feel that it is not appropriate for these ethical committees to adjudicate on studies based on samples drawn from public records and not involving any medical interventions, nevertheless, we feel these committees had a point. We hoped that the right to refuse to take part would mean that people could protect themselves against distress and that the people who did take part would find it helpful to talk to someone they did not know about their experiences and feelings. In the event although many people we talked to seemed to find our interviewers sympathetic and understanding, there were some informants who, in the opinion of their relatives at least, had been unnecessarily distressed by taking part in the study which revived painful memories. In our view it would be paternalistic to protect people against being asked to take part in such studies. But our efforts to ensure that people were not distressed by our study were not always totally successful as will be seen in the next chapter.

Dropping the areas covered by the two ethical committees who turned down our proposal endangered the representativeness of our sample. The effect of this will be examined in Chapter 8. It was suggested that we should select other areas as replacements but we rejected this on the grounds that the only scientific way to do this would be to take another random starting point and select a new set of twelve areas. There was no guarantee that we would do any better and that would have involved a further six months delay and more work. We did, however, increase our sample size slightly in each of the remaining areas, as described in the previous chapter.

One of the committees that turned us down covered only part of our study area – although it was the larger part. So, in effect, we were reduced to ten and a third areas. In the event, as we will relate in the next chapter, we had problems with the interviewer covering this part area. This led us to abandon that area altogether.

In conclusion

Our experience with ethical committees shows that standards and criteria vary between committees. It has not given us any confidence in the system or led us to feel that committees necessarily make their decisions on either rational or ethical grounds. This is supported by a recent study of diversity in the practice of district ethics committees (Gilbert, Fulford and Parker 1989) the results of which suggested that many committees are not functioning adequately and that the guidelines proposed by the Royal College of Physicians in 1984 have been largely ignored.

In our view the ethical issues to which the committees should have confined themselves related to the way we protected the confidentiality of the information given to us and the disclosure to us of data relating to individuals obtained by doctors and nurses in their professional capacity.

But the two ethical committees who did not approve our study did so because they did not think we should approach people identified from public records with a request for an interview. We recognise that the subject of our study could cause distress to some people even though it was likely to be helpful to others. We tried to minimise the potential for distress but did not always succeed. Even so we do not think medical ethical committees are the appropriate bodies to deal with such issues.

The present system is particularly ill equipped to deal with national studies covering several areas. A national ethics committee might facilitate such studies and it could monitor the workings of local ethics committees (see Lock 1990). In any event it would be helpful if there was some agreement on the nature of research studies that should be reviewed by ethical committees. The draft statement on local research ethics committees circulated by the Department of Health unfortunately does not consider the definition of research (Marshall and Moodie 1989).

Many of the existing committees seem to lack experience and expertise in assessing social studies. This is to be expected since probably most of the proposals submitted to them relate to drug trials or other medical or surgical interventions. Indeed, in our view, interview or postal surveys should only need to seek ethical approval if they are based on people selected from confidential records. Our study did not fall into this category and we submitted it to the ethical committees because of the demands of the MRC. As the study was approved by the committees in our ten remaining study areas this may have improved the response of officials to our requests for information and increased the response rates of doctors and nurses to our questionnaires.

5 Interviewing relatives and others about the people who died

The interviewing on this study was demanding in a number of respects – more so than in many of the other studies the Institute had done. The sampling meant that people dying in all sorts of different circumstances would have to be covered by the same questionnaire. In an emotionally stressful situation it was particularly important not to give offence by asking irrelevant questions, so there were a large number of instructions to interviewers to skip particular questions in certain circumstances. This increased the complexity of the intellectual task. The emotional demands were, if anything, more daunting as many of the interviews were with bereaved people remembering painful events. Our requirements for interviewers, then, were for people experienced in using complex structured questionnaires, and emotionally mature enough to cope with distress in respondents.

Recruitment and training

The Institute for Social Studies in Medical Care is a small organisation, with about five or six projects, usually at different stages, under way at any one time. Unlike the Office of Population Censuses and Surveys (OPCS) or Social and Community Planning Research (SCPR) our size does not justify the establishment of a permanent network of interviewers around the country. We are dependent on luck in choosing areas where we know of good interviewers living in or near the area, and on personal contacts with other research workers for recruiting our team of interviewers. In the last resort, advertisements in local newspapers are used.

For this study we needed two interviewers in each of the areas. Eighty death certificates in each area, along with a few extra hospice deaths in some, would mean that each person would have a list of about 40 interviews, a workload which we felt was reasonable for an interviewing period of about six weeks. We also wanted interviewers to get to know their colleague in their area, so that they could give each other mutual support in what would be a difficult task. They could also do 'therapeutic listening' to each other over the usual frustrations involved in interviewing: difficulty tracing people, finding them out, and broken appointments.

As far as possible we wanted interviewers with experience in social rather than market research. Past experience had shown that interviewers who had worked for OPCS or SCPR were generally well trained and experienced enough for our purposes. Those with a market research background tended to have had more superficial interviewing experience and would often require re-training.

We wrote to contacts in university and polytechnic departments, as well as other research units, and to interviewers we knew in the relevant areas. Recruiting for the northern areas proved more straightforward than some of the southern areas, and in the end our less experienced interviewers were all clustered in southern areas. In six areas we had to resort to newspaper advertisements.

Potential interviewers were sent a description of the project and asked to send in a CV and letter of application. We held interviews in Manchester and London for the jobs. All applicants – except ones we had worked with before and those who had worked for OPCS – completed an accuracy test and all were interviewed by both of us for half an hour.

Of the 24 interviewers who eventually worked on the project, eleven had either worked for OPCS or SCPR or both, seven had experience of other social research, and one had experience of market research only. Although we were sometimes unhappy about doing so, we recruited five who had no research interviewing experience at all, and had to be trained from scratch. All but one were women, partly because applicants were mostly women, but also because we felt men would be less likely to get a good response when knocking on the doors of elderly people. Recruitment proved difficult in two inner city areas that had been chosen. In one of them we were told by one person who applied, who worked for a market research firm, that her organisation would not send interviewers to the area we were proposing. However, in the end we found people who were prepared to work there, and our most difficult area for recruiting interviewers turned out not to be an inner city area.

The Institute for Social Studies in Medical Care pays interviewers by the hour with two different rates, one for time spent interviewing, and a lower rate (with a mileage allowance) for time spent travelling. Payment by the hour rather than by the interview was, we felt, important. Some days would be spent looking for people to interview without success, and the discouraging effect of this would be exacerbated if interviewers felt they were not being paid for their efforts. Payment by interview might also encourage cheating by fabricating interviews.

Briefings for interviewers were held for this part of the project in Manchester and London in April 1988. People with more substantial experience were required to attend for two days, and those with less experience for five days. Interviewers had been sent a package of papers to study beforehand, which included the questionnaires to be used and notes – both about survey research interviewing in general and about the use of the questionnaire. The format of the briefings consisted of time discussng the principles of interviewing (for the less experienced) followed by a detailed, step-by-step guide to the questionnaire. The rest of the time was spent in practice interviews, with one of us usually taking the role of respondent and interviewers taking turns to go through the questionnaire. Both of us had personal experiences of bereavement to draw upon as material for these practices, and a combination of these and imagined situations meant that we were able to create a sufficient variety of circumstances to cover the main situations interviewers were likely to encounter.

Our general aim in providing this practice was to give interviewers sufficient familiarity with the technical business of following the questionnaire instructions correctly, and writing down verbatim responses simultaneously, so that they would be able to focus on their relationship with respondents when faced with real interviews.

As a half way stage between practices and the actual interviewing, we required interviewers to complete two tape recorded practice interviews with people they knew who had been bereaved. These practice tapes, along with the completed questionnaires from them, were returned to the Institute where we listened to the tapes and checked the accuracy of the questionnaire record. Our notes on any discrepancies and errors and comments on their interviewing techniques were then sent back to interviewers as feedback. Practice tapes also helped us to identify those who were struggling with the task, and who required particular help and support – sometimes amounting to further practice sessions in an additional briefing time.

Providing feedback to interviewers did not end at this point. The first few interviews that any of the interviewers returned were checked closely for questions missed or asked in error. We also paid attention to the positive qualities of interviews and gave interviewers our reactions to this as well as accounts of errors. With some interviewers we were able to stop this feedback after the first few interviews were returned; with others the process went on for longer.

The confidentiality of all the information we received was stressed to interviewers, and when they accepted the job they signed an agreement about this. Respondents were also assured of confidentiality both orally before the start of the interview and in a written statement about the project that was left with them. Interviewers were issued with identity cards and the police in local areas were informed about the study, in case they received any inquiries from people who were approached about the survey.

People who dropped out

Three interviewers dropped out of this first part of the study, after doing some of the interviews. One experienced person whom we had imagined would cope well found herself, after three interviews, having nightmares about death. She took a break from the job for two weeks, and when she tried again found herself in the situation of provoking a family argument by her presence. This she found too much and she told us she could take no more. Relations with her were friendly thereafter, and she proved helpful in a number of ways when we were seeking interviews with professionals on the second part of the study.

The circumstances surrounding the second interviewer who dropped out were less straightforward. Her interviews stopped coming in to the office and a telephone call resulted in a story of overwhelming family commitments. We needed her help in handing over the interviews to a substitute interviewer, but subsequent calls to elicit this help were unsuccessful. She was avoiding us, and would not answer letters. This person was not an experienced interviewer and may well have found the emotional demands of the job too much to cope with, but we never learned the full story.

These two drop-outs may be seen as failures of our recruitment strategy and the subsequent support that we tried to give. With the first one, the decision to stop was unexpected, and less distressing for us as the interviewer was quite open about the reasons for what had happened. She had misjudged her own ability to cope with the emotional stress of the subject matter. With the second interviewer, with the benefit of hindsight, there were earlier indications that she was struggling which should have alerted us to problems. She worked in an area where we had found it hard to find interviewers and because of this difficulty we probably pressed her beyond her limits. In the event, one of us (CS) helped in completing her quota of interviews.

The third interviewer who dropped out illustrates the importance of checking interviewers' work. The Institute procedure meant that when a completed questionnaire was returned to the office certain checks were made comparing information gained in the interview with that on the death registration forms. Interviewers had been given the name and address of the deceased, their age at the time of death and for women their marital status, (a man's marital status is not given on the death registration form). They were also given the name and address of the person who registered the death and the relationship of this person to the deceased. The cause, the exact date of death and the place of death were known to us, but not to the interviewer who had to get this information from the respondent. This was used to check that interviewers were indeed doing the interviews and were not making them up.

Applying these routine checks revealed one interviewer who returned three questionnaires where these items of information were radically different from the death registration forms. Relatives are not always reliable sources of information. In particular, the date of death is not always recalled accurately and there is sometimes confusion about cause. However, the discrepancies in these three interviews went beyond normal levels of inaccuracy. Thus a man whose death registration form stated he had died of cancer of the oesophagus in hospital was said on the questionnaire to have died suddenly of 'Failure of something or other – heart attack' at home. Another man who on the death registration form was said to have died of cerebral glioma in a nursing home, was said on the questionnaire to have died suddenly of a 'stroke/heart attack' at home. The third interview was said to have been with a daughter who commented 'I'm glad he was at home' when her father had died at home after a week in bed following a fall. The death registration form stated the cause of death to be lung cancer, and that death occurred in hospital.

Such glaring inconsistencies were disturbing. Telephone calls to the people who were said to have been respondents revealed that in one case a refusal had been given. The matron of the nursing home where the man with cerebral glioma had died told us that he had been there for some weeks before his death.

We informed the interviewer of these discrepancies and asked for an explanation. The interviewer expressed surprise and suggested that there must have been a mix-up with the serial numbers. She asked for time in which she would try to sort out the muddle. Our own study of the serial numbers suggested that this explanation was unlikely as none of the death registration forms relating to the other interviews she had been given matched the data she recorded in these three disputed interviews. An exchange of letters began, with the interviewer persisting with claims that there had been confusion over serial numbers. Her final word was that she would need to go back to all her addresses and look at the houses in order to jog her memory about the interviews. We declined to finance such an enterprise. In any event, a fundamental error, of putting the wrong serial numbers on interviews, cast doubt on the acccuracy of the rest of her work. If this explanation about serial numbers was incorrect, the consequences were even more serious.

Eventually we decided that we would use none of the interviews she had done. This decision was made easier because she was working in the area where one of the two health authorities involved had refused ethical permission for the study. We were only seeking 23 interviews in the remaining half of the area. Nevertheless, the cost of training and paying for the interviews that had been returned was considerable, so we were disappointed at the loss. We were left with ten study areas from the original twelve.

The experience of interviewing

When all the fieldwork for the study was completed, in April 1989, we sent 21 of the interviewers who had worked on the study a questionnaire asking for their accounts of the work (the other three were unavailable). Seventeen were returned, including one by an interviewer who had only worked on the second half of the study interviewing doctors and nurses. The questionnaire asked for comments about both parts of the study (that is, the first part involving interviews with relatives and others who knew the people who had died, and the second part interviewing doctors and nurses) in answer to the following questions:

– What did you like about this part of the study?
– What did you dislike about it?
– How well/badly did the briefing prepare you for (this) part?

A final question asked:

– How did your work for this project compare with other interviewing work you have done?

The very full and helpful answers to these questions form the basis of what follows.

The initial briefing. All but two of the sixteen interviewers who
attended the briefing and returned questionnaires recorded that the
briefing had helped in preparing them. Contact with other interviewers was mentioned as helpful by two, and the close attention to detail
was mentioned by one, who wrote:

> The briefing was excellent, particularly the mock interviews. I was
> dreading that as I felt rather stupid and inadequate. It soon tran-
> spired that we all had a lot to learn! Ann and Clive's attention to
> detail and persistence in "getting it right" really paid off ..... I still
> made mistakes but think that there would have been more but for
> the briefing.

Another felt that the practice 'gave me the confidence so that I could
concentrate on the right relationship with the informant.'

However, although the general tenor of comments about the briefing were positive, criticisms were made. The two interviewers who
felt that the briefing had not been helpful both did their fieldwork in
tough, inner city areas. One wrote in response to the question about
how well the briefing had prepared her:

> Not very well. I found it wasn't always relevant. The first time I
> did a more well off, more intelligent (I don't know how else to
> phrase it) carer it all seemed to fit and make sense, and it was such a
> relief.

Another who felt well prepared by virtue of her previous experience
of similar work as much as by the briefing, expressed a concern
(which we shared) that less experienced interviewers might have felt
less well prepared.

The approach to respondents. The method of approach – knocking
unannounced on the door of the residence of the deceased or the
informant to the registrar – made many of the interviewers feel
apprehensive. In fact, the approach was specifically singled out by
five of the sixteen as an aspect of the study they disliked. For example:

> I found the initial approach the hardest part .... I detested door-

stepping. It took a lot of courage for me to pluck up the energy to go and knock on a door.

I was still nervous about it when I did my last interview.

The fear of being seen as an intruder, and the further fear of an aggressive response were at the root of this, and this was heightened by knowing little about the circumstances of the death. We were asking the interviewers to step into a strange house, enquiring about events that could be emotionally highly charged. The sense of danger was increased by the physical surroundings in some areas:

> (What did you dislike about it?): The terrible blocks of flats – the filth, the smell. Which was more disgusting or frightening, the lifts or the stairs? The lifts – I didn't know who would be in them, and they always seemed to be breaking down, the stink in them! ..... The stairs were many, hard and frightening, with dog and human excrement and urine on them. The windows broken or boarded up, piles of broken glass, bottles and rubbish on each stair. Graffiti everywhere. The boys (some about ten or twelve) staggering around – I suppose glue sniffers. Flats where no-one was ever there and neighbours knew nothing about them (or said they didn't) ..... How I admire doctors, nurses and social workers who have to do home visits .....

Two interviewers made the point that where the death had been violent – either suicide or murder, they should have been told the cause of death so as to be prepared for the situation. Refusals, or the manner of them, were mentioned by seven as an aspect of the study they disliked, and this was explicitly linked by some to the unpleasant feeling that they were intruders into personal matters:

> (A) few respondents ..... really resented any attempt to interview them. They regarded the whole thing as an intrusion.

> I didn't get many refusals, but when I did I felt it was mostly from those who were just hanging on after their ordeal, so I suppose I disliked being viewed as someone who might possibly tip them over the edge.

One of the two interviewers who dropped out of the study after starting interviews had done so after a particularly bad experience, when the wife of the deceased had come into the house where the daughter was being interviewed. The interviewer wrote us a letter saying that 'there followed a very unpleasant scene, the mother very irate and crying, the daughter crying and the brother-in-law asking me to leave ..... I was very shaken by the whole affair .....'

On occasion, a further death had occurred in the family:

> (There was) a daughter whose husband had died the night before I called to interview her about her father who had died in 1987. She was so distressed and misunderstood, thinking I wanted to interview her about her husband. This was very distressing.

Our decision about how to approach potential respondents was influenced by two factors. First, it was only after enquiries at the addresses concerned that the correct person could be identified; in many cases the information on the death registration form would have been inadequate in supplying the name and address of a relevant person to write to. Secondly, there was a concern that writing to respondents beforehand would create anxieties that could not then be dealt with by an interviewer being there on the spot to answer any questions.

In addition to the worries about intruding, interviewers also mentioned other, more mundane, difficulties with the approach. Two referred to difficulties in deciding who the best respondent would be. Interviewers were asked to record at the end of each interview whether they felt the person they had just been talking to had been the most appropriate person to have interviewed. For five per cent of the 639 interviews returned this was not the case, and in a further 9% interviewers were uncertain. A typical situation here was where the person who knew most about the deceased's circumstances felt it would be too upsetting and some other member of the family took over.

Another interviewer referred to the frustration felt at the end of some days spent travelling to empty houses or receiving refusals, when the whole day produced no interviews. In fact, 34% of the completed interviews were done on the first call to an address; 39% took three or more calls, and ten interviews were done after eight or more calls.

Having someone to talk to. On the other hand, these examples of difficulties should be set in a general context of helpfulness shown to the interviewers. The apprehension and nervousness was often followed by a good experience:

> At first I thought I might feel I was too intrusive, as grief is a very personal thing but ..... most people felt better for talking so it was all right ..... Considering it was a 'cold' call ..... I was very pleasantly surprised at the good response.

Thirteen of the interviewers mentioned that they felt the experience of being interviewed had helped people, by giving them someone to talk to about their feelings. One instance of this is of interest, in that it shows a situation which could have turned out badly (like some of the instances above) but which changed into something entirely more helpful to all concerned:

> I remember in particular talking to (a) widow who was in floods of tears and didn't want me to leave. (Her) daughter arrived, very belligerent, but her mother stressed that I was helping her. The interview took a long time (and) I re-called the following day and saw both mother and daughter who greeted me very warmly, and yet another cup of tea!!

Some interviewers felt that the reason why certain people found the interview helpful was that they had not had the opportunity to talk to anyone else:

> Several respondents said that the interview was the first time they had been able to talk about their grief, and felt better for having done it.

> People on the whole, with very few exceptions, were pleased to see me and to be able to talk freely. Many of them seemed to feel a real sense of frustration at not having seen anyone, outside their families, with whom they could discuss how they felt ..... I'd never actually believed before that former friends crossed the road rather than having to talk to someone who'd been bereaved. Some respondents recognised that this was due to embarrassment, but nevertheless resented it.

Many informants were tearful, but at the end they were thanking me for listening and said that they had not been able to talk to anyone in this way since the death – relatives were too emotionally involved and others could not understand. Men appreciated the opportunity to talk especially – they don't always get the back-up that women do ..... One man said he had not talked about his wife's death to anyone – he was afraid of breaking down. He said it was a great relief to talk to someone he would not see again.

I found most people liked to have someone to talk to about their loved ones and I was surprised how often I was told 'I haven't talked about this with anyone else.'

Beyond this immediate, almost therapeutic, benefit that some people appeared to derive from the interview was a moral benefit which one interviewer identified:

I liked the comfort that some bereaved relatives were able to derive from the idea that their experiences, and those of their dead relatives, could be of interest and potential help to other people in similar circumstances.

However, this argument was not always convincing:

(Some) said they supposed it would all end up on a shelf and was a waste of money but they agreed to help.

Technique and coping with the questionnaire. Eleven interviewers made criticisms of the questionnaire and three were complimentary. The chief problem identified (by seven interviewers) was that the questionnaire was too long or was repetitive:

(What did you dislike?) Definitely the length of the questionnaire which in my opinion was quite exhausting for most old people. Their concentration and attention span could not cope with it.

I did feel the length of the questionnaire was occasionally a hurdle.

Several informants got bored with the schedule. They found it repetitive – they would say 'I've just told you that' and once or twice they really got very tired of the interview.

Ten per cent of the 639 interviews lasted less than an hour according to the records interviewers made at the end of each interview. Fifty-six per cent took between one and two hours, 27% took between two and three hours and 7% took more than three hours to complete. Most (96%) were done in one sitting and all but one of the rest were done in two.

Interviews that tended to take a long time were those where the illness had caused several hospitalisations as well as home nursing care. The questionnaire provided for up to two hospitals and two types of home nursing to be asked about. If the person who died also had a lot of symptoms, the number of things that were asked about would mount up significantly and resulted in some of the longer interviews.

Three interviewers said they found some of the questions intrusive or insensitive. An example given was a question asking respondents to describe how good their relationship was with the deceased. One made the pertinent comment that the questions on whether people knew they were dying seemed designed for people with malignant disease. Asking about an elderly, frail person whether they knew they were going to die was felt to be inappropriate in some cases: the answer was likely to be 'Of course, she was 90!' In fact, the literature on the communication of a terminal prognosis is one that has usually assumed the younger cancer patient as a model. One of the findings from the survey has been that a diagnosis of dying is less easy in conditions that are not cancer, and the corresponding 'moment of truth' is less clear cut.

Although the majority of comments about the questionnaire were critical, there were three which were complimentary. One interviewer felt that:

> ..... the Institute's questionnaires are brilliant and well formulated compared with some (others) I'm working on now ..... I have become a questionnaire critic and immensely boring on the subject.

Doing these interviews required a complex set of skills and the balancing of sometimes conflicting requirements. On the one hand accuracy was important: questions had to be asked as worded and instructions to skip followed or else the question sequence would not fit the circumstances of the respondents. Answers had to be recorded accurately and we had emphasised to interviewers in the briefings that as much comment as possible should be written down verbatim. To facilitate this the questionnaire had been designed as a booklet, with a blank page opposite each page of questions for extended comments to be written. At the same time interviewers needed to concentrate on their relationship with the person they were talking to. A major purpose of the briefing had been to give interviewers confidence in their knowledge of the questionnaire – particularly the skips appropriate in various circumstances – so that they could concentrate on the other things they had to do. This combination of skills was experienced by some as particularly demanding:

> This was the most difficult interviewing I have ever done, I found it more satisfying because it required a greater level of skill – it was more demanding ..... I developed my skills and required a new one: after a while I got nicely competent at listening and recording simultaneously.

In addition, interviewers had the problem – familiar to anyone who has used a structured questionnaire – of keeping respondents to the point so that the relevant questions were answered. We had told interviewers that they should be prepared to listen to what respondents wanted to tell them even if it was not relevant to the study, or even though they mentioned things that would be asked about later in the interview as it might be that there was something they wanted to get off their chests and until they had done that they would not be able to concentrate on the interview questions. However, some respondents talked irrelevantly because they were like that anyway. Four interviewers identified the need to keep people on the point. For example:

> A bit of the trouble was they would tell me how good/bad the district nurses were before I got to the questions – despite me telling them 'I'll come to that in a little while.'

People's memories of events were not always clear:

> As with other projects you realise how muddled people are about who they've actually seen. 'Some doctor' or 'a lady from the hospital or hospice – she may be a nurse, I don't know.' No-one seems sure.

This complex interviewing task, then, was sometimes exacerbated by special circumstances:

> (What did you dislike?) Trying to interview in a room full of people – a Pakistani family very upset by father's death and mother unable to speak English.

> (What did you dislike?) Having to cope a few times with people who had suffered another bereavement since the one we were discussing or there was another loss which they would have preferred to talk about.

The emotional impact of interviewing. References to the harrowing or emotionally draining nature of the interviews were common in the questionnaires that were returned. Thus one interviewer who had been a social worker wrote:

> I found interviewing the relatives to be most draining physically and mentally – more so than my other interviewing I have carried out. This includes counselling bereaved parents after the death of a loved child.

This interviewer found that:

> ...for the majority the wounds were too new and they were not through the grieving stage. It was necessary for me to spend some time with them after the questionnaire had been completed before I felt comfortable leaving them.

One interviewer found it difficult to know what to do when people cried:

> I disliked upsetting people by my questions. Several of them broke down and wept during the interviews and I felt personally inadequate. I could only sympathise in general terms, not knowing the deceased.

Others felt more able to accept the feelings of distress that the interview was provoking and became drawn into the respondent's world:

> Most people were very brave and eager to help .... Tears were shed, not just by them! .... The real delight was getting to know

people. When you spend a great deal of time listening to the last year of someone's life it is inevitable that you hear much, much more ..... I loved sitting and listening and found it hard, sometimes, to remember why I was there.

Deaths of younger people were identified by two interviewers as being particular sources of stress:

> I did not exactly dislike, but found harrowing, the few interviews – mostly where younger people had died – where respondents became really upset. There are about three I remember where the respondent cried throughout the interview, and this is the only project I've worked on where I had difficulty in not crying along with them.

> It was very sad when the person who died was young, especially in traumatic circumstances ..... From a purely personal point of view regarding these sorts of cases with the young, I tried to imagine how devastated I would have felt if this had happened to my own children! I couldn't imagine how you would ever get over it.

Balancing the need to maintain objectivity and detachment with situations where people's grief produced feelings of distress in the interviewer was, then, at times found difficult. Some interviewers seem to have coped with this better than others. It was often difficult to resist the desire to help in some practical way:

> Sometimes, in cases where I did get an interview, where the bereaved was left very much alone and lonely, I came away feeling desperately sad and unhappy and really wanting to do something to help their plight, but not able to of course.

Although many of the comments were reports of refusals, difficulties and stresses, it should be remembered that the response rate to the survey was 80% and that the people interviewed were not always close to the deceased or particularly upset. Thirty-six per cent of respondents were spouses and 26% children of the deceased, but 21% were friends, neighbours or officials. Interviewers were asked to record at the end of each interview whether the informant had cried or expressed emotion in other ways during the interview. Twenty-two per cent had cried, and 21% had expressed emotion in other ways without crying, which means that in over half the interviews the respodent had not become overtly upset. One interviewer wrote:

> I did not find many carers were very upset. For most it was a blessed relief as the old person had been ill a long time.

As well as the stressful moments, a number of interviewers also commented on the general helpfulness of the people they met:

> The more I think back, I met some lovely people and learned a lot.

> I was pleasantly surprised at how helpful people were. Some couldn't wait to tell me how well they'd been looked after, others to criticise the medical profession and system in general and others who said if it would be helpful to me they would agree to the interview.

This welcoming attitude on the part of most people was obviously encouraging for the interviewers, and offset some of the the stressful moments.

Most worrying from an ethical point of view were the occasional situations where an interview proceeded without much emotional arousal, but the emotional impact was felt afterwards by the respondent. Two or three cases occurred where complaints were made to us about the interview. An example is as follows:

> A widow was interviewed about her husband's illness and death. The interviewer had been asked in immediately and plied with tea, the widow showing the interviewer around the house. Her chief complaint about the care her husband had received related to the hospital treatment, and she had considered making a formal complaint. A day after the interview her daughter rang the Institute office, angry that her mother had been interviewed and had been upset again by being made to remember the circumstances. Her mother had been through a very difficult time, said the daughter, and the interview had stirred things up again. The interviewer later reported that the daughter had previously tried hard to dissuade her mother from complaining about the hospital treatment, and the interview had revived the widow's feelings of injustice.

One of the ethical committees who refused permission for our project had made the point that the interviewing could stir up problems and create a demand for bereavement counselling with which their service could not cope. We do not know how many people were 'stirred up' in this way, or whether being so affected was necessarily a destructive or negative experience. We have only the view of many of the interviewers that they felt many respondents benefitted from the opportunity to talk. In the few instances where things went wrong (either a situation where an interviewer initiated a family 'scene' or where a complaint was made to the Institute) it was relatives who made the complaint rather than the respondents themselves.

What interviewers gained

Some of the experiences the interviewers valued were similar to those in other surveys: the opportunity to glimpse into the lives of people different from themselves, the chance to learn about the family relationships or the social history of the local area and seeing new places.

Some interviewers reflected in general terms on what they had learned about death and dying:

(What did you like?) Becoming more aware of how unpredictable life is and therefore how precious every day is.

Personally I gained a lot from doing this work. Listening to people talking about death and dying and understanding what the experience had meant to them made death familiar and much less frightening to me.

It was as always interesting to hear other people's experience of events and particularly in this instance since these were among the most, if not the most, important of their lives. From a selfish point of view it provided the interviewer with material that could be used to refer to when dealing with experiences maybe closer to home ..... I think we were privileged as interviewers to share the experiences of these people, and to learn from them ..... (I did) succeed in building up a picture of the situation relating to a period of life which is a proving ground for what has gone before and also is for many a test of their own and the deceased's worth to those around them.

Support from the Institute. Six of the interviewers commented on the quality of support from the Institute. Two appreciated the straight-forward organisation and the flexibility of deadlines, as well as the fact that as much time could be spent with relatives as was needed:

> I liked being able to give as much time to the interviewee as they needed so that I could leave feeling reasonably comfortable after possibly experiencing a lot of grief ..... The administrative proce-dures were better than I've encountered elsewhere – simple proce-dures and no loads of forms to fill in ..... I particularly liked not being under pressure and having flexible deadlines.

Five were appreciative of the quality of support. For example:

> I felt 'the management' were always available to chat to if I had any worries ..... it was nice to be kept informed of the progress of others ..... I always felt I was 'part' of the survey and that you knew me and were interested in how I was doing – not only as far as numbers of interviews ... but how I felt and was I enjoying the work – all very important when interviewing can be an isolated sort of job.

Although no criticisms of the conditions of work and support were made by the interviewers who returned questionnaires, it should be noted that the two interviewers who dropped out of the survey did not return questionnaires, and may have had different feelings.

6 Collecting information from doctors and nurses

One of the features of Institute studies over the years has been to gather the views and experiences of both the providers and receivers of health care. Looking at issues from different viewpoints can reveal mismatches in expectations, different perceptions of the importance of certain things and identify gaps in the records of professionals, or the recall of patients. For Life before death we aimed to get the accounts of hospital doctors and nurses involved in particular episodes of care, and to find out their general views of services available in the area. We did not ask general practitioners about individual patients, only about their views and experiences of caring for the dying. Experience on the earlier study of Life before death had shown them to have difficulty in recalling details of patients who had died as the notes had been returned to the Family Practitioner Committee. Tracing the relatives and friends of people who die by door-to-door enquiries is relatively straightforward compared to discovering the names and addresses of their medical and nursing attendants. What follows is a descripton of the various exercises that were involved in identifying, approaching and interviewing these people.

The general practitioners

This part of the study was relatively simple. Most of our informants were able to give the name and address of the general practitioner of the person who had died, and a reasonable response rate from a postal questionnaire to these general practitioners was achieved.

In fact, of the 639 people for whom interviews were gained, in 87% of cases the doctor was named. In addition, two general practitioners were identified by relatives who otherwise did not wish to be interviewed. For 2% the doctor was known to have died or retired and for another 2% the person was in a hospital all year so the respondent was not asked. Two of the people who died had no general practitioner. For the rest the general practitioner was not known. Our experience on the pilot had led us to ask interviewers to obtain lists of local general practitioners against which they could check names and addresses. Eventually the total number of general practitioners to be surveyed was 397 (some patients had the same general practitioner). Three mailings produced a response rate of 62%.

In addition to information which the doctors provided about

themselves, the Department of Health and Social Security were able to provide centrally recorded information about the doctors' characteristics, such as their age, country of qualification, whether they were designated as trainers of general practitioners and the size of the practice. Whether they were members of the Royal College of General Practitioners was obtained from the Medical Register. This information was entered on the computer along with the questionnaire data.

Hospital and hospice doctors

Our experience of the pilot had been that people rarely remembered the name of the consultant under whom the person who had died was admitted. The best we could hope for, in most cases, was the name of the hospital. The main study proved no different from the pilot in this respect. Identifying the consultant who gave care to the people in the sample involved a major exercise of writing to the hospitals and hospices concerned. It was important to complete this exercise as quickly as possible, since as time passed memories of the patients concerned were likely to fade, records of their admissions would be filed away ever deeper in the recesses of the system, and medical staff would be more likely to have moved on to other posts in other hospitals.

We had to wait until all the questionnaires were returned for a particular area before writing to the hospital managers concerned, since we did not want to be adding patients to the lists we sent them. Similarly, we had to wait until all the hospital managers for a particular area replied before we could start to approach the doctors. Our experience of the pilot showed that it was common for consultants to work in more than one hospital in an area, and we wanted to write to each consultant with a complete list of his or her patients, and not add a patient every time another hospital manager replied to our request. We were therefore dependent on the slowest interviewer and the slowest hospital manager in each of the areas to complete the exercise.

One-hundred-and-forty-five hospitals and hospices were identified by respondents as places where inpatient care had been given (this figure, and others in this and the next section, includes the seven extra hospice deaths for whom interviews were obtained). A total of 747 hospital episodes were involved (one hospital episode being defined as one or more admission to a single hospital or hospice in the twelve months before death). Six-hundred-and-thirty-nine episodes were reported by respondents, and a further 108 were gathered from the death registration forms of people for whom no interview was obtained. In some instances hospitals were grouped into units under a single general manager, so fewer than 145 hospital managers were involved.

We sent each hospital manager a letter explaining the purpose of the study and asking for their help in identifying the names of consultants under whom certain patients were admitted. A list of the patients, their addresses, their dates of death, age and whether they died in that hospital was enclosed. After four weeks a reminder letter was sent. These two mailings produced a response of only 32%, and these tended to be hospitals to which few of our sample had been admitted.

Persistent and regular telephone calls, with careful recording of what was said at each call, were now the order of the day. For some weeks one of us was to spend afternoons on the telephone, trying to get through to the correct person and establish what was happening to the request. One of the message sequences conveys the difficulties that could arise:

Date	Message
20/7/88	– Original letter sent.
17/8	– The manager has moved to Hospital D and now covers both this and Hospital C. Secretary will telephone me.
1/9	– Engaged.
6/9	– Engaged.
10/9	– Wrote again.
27/9	– Secretary has just received the letter. She will ring me tomorrow afternoon and tell me the manager's decision.
3/10	– No return call. I ring secretary who says it has been passed to the Patient Services Manager (PSM).
13/10	– Secretary to PSM says she will get him to ring me.
17/10	– No return call. PSM says he never received anything from the general manager.
17/10	– Left message for secretary to general manager to ring me *urgently*.
20/10	– No return call. I talk to PSM again who now says he has the request and is 'actioning it', which sounds very vigorous. I am impressed by his manner. It sounds as if he will get things done.

25/10 – The action has led to nothing so far. Left message for PSM to ring me. No return call.

27/10 – Got him! He'll see how its going and ring me back. No return call.

7/11 – At 2.35 p.m. I speak to PSM who says he'll ring me in ten minutes. No return call. At 3.05 p.m. I reach PSM again. He tells me that someone else is now dealing with it and she will ring me this afternoon. No return call.

8/11 – The 'someone else' rings me! It was sent yesterday, first class post.

9/11 – Arrival of information. Thank you letter sent.

To be fair to the hospitals, this was one of the more difficult cases. Our misfortune was, as explained earlier, that we had to wait for the last of the cases to come through with the information before we could start the survey. A rough count of the telephone messages recorded in this exercise comes to 204.

Of the 747 patient episodes we were able to get consultants' names for 639 (86%) of them. This involved a total of 333 consultants. Excluding episodes that we just knew about from information on death registration forms for people for whom an interview was not given, of the 639 episodes reported we got consultants names for 536 (84%), involving 301 consultants. Although it took a long time almost all the hospitals replied in the end. Only five did not reply at all. Three wrote to say they could not or would not help. For the rest, there were some instances where the consultant had died or moved on, and a few where the hospital records did not show the patient to have been admitted. In spite of the difficulties and delays, it must be said that the hospital records systems were remarkably effective in identifying past patients. This was in marked contrast to the community nurses.

So by November, in most areas, a year or more after the deaths were registered, we were in a position to write to the consultants involved. We explained the purpose of the study and asked them for two things. We were sending them a postal questionnaire asking for their general views and experiences of caring for patients who died. This could be returned in a reply paid envelope. We also asked them to nominate someone in the hospital who had cared for particular patients who had been admitted under them. Of course, where permission had been refused by a relative for us to pursue enquiries about the medical care of the deceased we did not ask the consultant for this. This meant that, as this affected 112 of the episodes for which we had a consultant's name, our sample size was 527 (71% of the hospital episodes reported by respondents or derived from registration forms in the first part of the study). Nominees could be the consultants themselves, or a more junior doctor or a nurse on the ward. We adopted this approach of encouraging consultants to nominate others because on the pilot we had experienced both a low response rate and consultants who could not remember the patients concerned. We thought nomination might help with both these problems. In the event, of the interviews we got, 62% were with the consultants themselves, 38% being with nominees. Nomination had its own problems, as junior medical staff in particular were likely to have moved to other posts since the patients had been in hospital.

Enclosed with the letter to consultants were copies of the consent forms signed by relatives. Consultants were also told of ethical committee approval of the study and were assured that information given would be treated confidentially. Three weeks after the letter was sent to consultants, the interviewers began telephoning to remind those who had not replied, and to try and make appointments for interviews. They encountered great difficulties.

Telephoning consultants is, if anything, more frustrating than telephoning general managers. The secretarial support is more likely to be part-time, and the doctors are less likely to be in their office or, even, on site. There is also the strange phenomenon of the disappearing letter. For some reason consultants' post quite frequently does not seem to reach them. Presumably it arrives at the hospital gate as frequently as any other post addressed to a particular place, but between hospital entrance and secretary's desk the passage of letters becomes less smooth. When interviewers rang the consultants' secretaries a common response was that the secretary had never seen the letter, knew nothing about the survey 'and you had better send it all again.' So we did, for a large number of the doctors. Occasionally we did it yet again.

The postal questionnaire was returned by 216 (65%) of the consultants; interviews about specific patients were gained in 249 (47%) cases.

Community nurses

Respondents for 227 patients reported nurses having provided care at home, with 56 of these reporting more than one sort of nurse (for example, a patient who received visits from district nurses and Mac-Millan nurses). We wanted to interview one of each type of nurse from whom the patient received care, with a limit of two types of nurse (that is, two nursing episodes) per patient, so we needed to identify the names of nurses in 283 episodes of nursing care.

Although hospital managers took a long time and a lot of reminding before they replied, we felt the exercise in identifying the names of consultants had been quite successful. The community nurses were much harder to identify, and this was largely due to the lack of efficient central records systems in health authorities. Sixteen health authorities were involved in the ten study areas. A useful publication, the *Handbook of Community Nursing*, (Wroe, 1987) gave the names and addresses of the people in charge of community nursing services in each health authority and we wrote to them with an explanatory letter and a request for help in identifying the names of nurses who gave care to a list of patients whose details were enclosed.

None of the community nurse managers replied to the letter, so phone calls began. It was more difficult to get information from these managers than the hospital managers, and a total of 92 calls were made. Further calls were needed in two districts where the managers asked us to write to and telephone individual health centres. In one of the most difficult areas it took fourteen telephone calls to establish that the director of nursing services was not going to help us, but wanted us to communicate with six health centres to find out the names. Although the director said she had informed the relevant practice managers in these health centres of the study, she had not, in fact, done so and new letters and explanations had to be given to each of the six practice managers. Thirty-one telephone calls were made to follow up these letters and the end result in that area was that we got the names of eight district nurses out of 21 nursing episodes. In another area the nurse manager insisted that it was health authority policy not to release the names of its staff to people outside the authority. She said we would have to write to the nurses concerned through her to ask their permission for their names to be given to us. We designed a special consent form and letter, but the exercise proved a waste of time as the records system in that area was not adequate to identify the nurses concerned. Only one nurse there was successfully identified.

Another problem arose in an area where the eventual outcome was a refusal by the manager to help. Her staff were too busy, she felt, and needed protection from extra demands.

Other nurse managers were more helpful and their records systems relatively more efficient and complete. Forty-six per cent of the nursing episodes were eventually assigned to a named nurse, involving 102 different nurses. In two cases the person we interviewed had identified only one type of nurse, but the nurse manager identified two types. In one case the person we approached refused an interview but gave us the names of two types of nurse who had visited the patient. All these were added to our total sample of nurses. Once interviewing started the response was remarkably good, and a welcome change from the difficulties we had with consultants. In some areas 100% of the nurses identified gave interviews and returned postal questionnaires, with the eventual response rate being 92% for the general questionnaire and 87% for the specific patient questionnaire. Most of the nurses' questionnaires were completed in face-to-face interviews: 91% of the general questionnaires and 90% of the questionnaires about specific patients. A few were completed by telephone (6% and 9%) and a few by post (2% and 1%). For 70% of the interviews about specific patients, nurses had records available and for 76% of these (52% of the interviews) nurses referred to the notes during the interview. Very few of the nurses said they had not received the letter sent to them, which suggests that consultants may be unusual in their difficulties over this. The interviewers experienced the approach to nurses as a welcome relief. We felt the same way.

The experience of interviewing

The briefing. The briefing for the second part of the study was a single day, spent introducing the questionnaires and talking through the approach to doctors and nurses. The interviewing task was less demanding than it had been on the first part – the questionnaires were shorter and less complicated. The briefing was also an opportunity for inteviewers from different areas to meet again and compare experiences of the first part of the study.

The less intense nature of the second briefing is reflected in the comments on interviewers' questionnaires. Most recorded that the briefing was 'fine', 'quite good preparation' and so on. Two mentioned how nice it was to meet the others again. Two stated that in retrospect they had been unprepared for how difficult it was going to be to contact the doctors, and one of these suggested that 'in retrospect I think Ann and Clive knew this was going to be particularly difficult but weren't letting on.'

One interviewer recorded that the briefing had been 'no help at all.'

The approach. A quotation from one interviewer conveys the frustration that all expressed in one form or another with the approach to hospital doctors:

> It began with the first contact: 'You must be joking. Christmas is only four weeks away, and after that they all go skiing' – these weren't the only reasons! I sent three sets of questionnaires to some consultants. Some sent them back with a terse refusal, others at least did the postal questionnaire ..... One consultant I spoke to was extremely patronising and rude to me on the telephone. Some gave contacts who had disappeared, wards and hospitals reorganised, closed down even! It was one big wild goose chase.

Another interviewer compared the experience to being like a double glazing salesman. Four mentioned the phenomenon of doctors and secretaries claiming not to have received our letter, as well as general difficulties. For example:

> (What did you dislike?) The difficulty in making appointments with the doctors. Their secretaries were most helpful but it did mean 'phoning and 'phoning and issuing duplicate questionnaires in so many cases, waiting for 'phone backs that never came. Early on I began to wonder if I would ever get an interview!

Opinion was divided on the helpfulness of secretaries. Three praised them, one describing them as 'invaluable', another saying that it was the secretaries who had made this part of the study possible. However, secretaries were also criticised, in both cases by interviewers who had themselves worked as doctors' secretaries:

> I found it very difficult, in many cases, to get beyond the secretaries and still don't know whether some of the consultants were shown the questionnaires. It was amazing how many 'hadn't seen' the original questionnaire.

> (secretaries) are so ready to ignore something like a questionnaire, hoping it will just disappear. They do have an enormous amount of paperwork to do daily.

The last interviewer found it a great advantage that she knew some of the staff involved, and was able to go into the hospital and talk face-to-face with the people concerned in order to arrange interviews.

Although the difficulties in contacting doctors was great, two interviewers mentioned that doing interviews by appointment, rather than by 'cold' calling as in the first part of the study, was welcome:

> It was very nice to be able to ring up and make appointments rather than going and knocking on people's doors.

The community nurses with whom interviews were sought were experienced as much more helpful than the doctors. All but two of the interviewers commented on how ready the nurses were to help with the survey. The two who did not say this noted that in their areas difficulties were experienced because a number of nurses were off sick. Two interviewers commented that district nurses went to great efforts to get the notes of the patients concerned. Typical comments here were:

> I found interviewing the nurses very easy, they were most co-operative, in many cases had gone to a lot of trouble to get the notes. It was quite easy to make appointments and the appointments were kept.

> The nurses were so helpful though all of them were extremely busy and under a lot of pressure. They did all they could to help and were most apologetic if they had to cancel an interview.

The interviews. The helpfulness of the community nurses was associated with a positive impression given to some interviewers about the quality of nurses' work. Four commented on the dedication, professionalism and the caring approach that the nurses conveyed. For example:

> Meeting the nurses was a pleasant experience. I was met with kindness and cordiality and was very impressed by their dedication and caring attitude. Many of them were doing work far beyond what their jobs required . . .

> I was very impressed, especially with the community nurses, the

amount of care and real concern they had for their patients . . . . All the community nurses that I interviewed were so dedicated, working long hours . . . . they really are angels of mercy and do a tremendous job.

No criticisms were expressed of community nurses themselves, but a few comments were made about the circumstances in which interviewing took place. We had found on the pilot that community nurses were more likely to agree to telephone interviews than were doctors, and one interviewer who had done one of these said she found it less satisfying than face-to-face interviews. Another said that, unlike doctors, nurses did not seem to have a private place to go to in order to do the interviews and this made things difficult.

One interviewer found that doctors were keen to discuss their views:

Of the doctors who did participate I found they also were keen to talk about their views of death and had had very little opportunity to do so in such depth.

Interviewers' experience of doctors was variable, and is well summarised by the following comment:

The interviews with doctors were quite an eye-opener: ranging from consultants who knew the cases without reference to notes and others who could not remember the patients even when they had read through all the notes.

Six of the interviewers mentioned doctors' difficulty in recalling patients, some linking this to the difficulty in retrieving notes and the time that had passed since the hospital episode (between 18 months and two years).

Some consultants knew very little about patients who had died and couldn't help with anyone who would know more. Lapse of time between deaths and interviews didn't help.

The majority of them didn't remember the patients and in fact had never actually seen the patients concerned and the doctors to whom they had delegated the patient care were often – mostly – no longer at that hospital.

The unavailability of notes in hospitals was terrible, so however co-operative the consultants wanted to be they couldn't help.

Two interviewers noted that the questionnaire was perceived by doctors as relating to patients with cancer, or who were dying. Since we were asking about any hospital admission during the last twelve months of life, our questions about death were sometimes felt to be irrelevant in some circumstances. Another interviewer observed that questions asking doctors to give rough estimates in terms of percentages of the proportion of patients for which certain symptoms could be controlled were experienced as inaccurate and unscientific by some doctors.

Interviewing on this study compared with other work

We asked the interviewers how their work on the project had compared with other work they had done. Three with market research experience compared the experience favourably:

This work was much more satisfying and interesting than most interviewing work though emotionally demanding . . .

I found this more interesting than market research work I have done.

I always found social studies more rewarding and satisfying. Commercial research often made me feel that I was rather exploiting the public . . . I did feel that, at times, I had perhaps been of some help to the bereaved.

Of those who had not done market research, three either had no previous interviewing experience or felt they could not answer the question. Eight compared their work on the study favourably but one did not, saying that the questionnaire needed improving and that there had been too much telephoning on the second part.

One who had found the work satisfying had reservations as well:

This was the most difficult interviewing I have done. I found it more satisfying because it required a greater level of skill – more demanding. On the other hand, although I liked doing this work I would not want to be always interviewing on such a serious subject and it is refreshing to change to a new subject each time it happens.

Finally, an interviewer summarised her view of the work in the following way:

It was among the more memorable surveys – and better than most.

7 Coding, data entry, computing and analysis

When we first planned this book we did not include a chapter on these topics. This is symptomatic of the lack of status often accorded to these essential processes in doing a survey. Coding and data entry in particular are the Cinderellas of survey method, attracting little academic interest or concern compared with sampling, interviewing and tests of significance. Yet a survey, like the proverbial chain, is probably as good as its weakest link. And if enough care, thought and time are not devoted to these aspects of the study the validity and usefulness of the whole operation are jeopardized.

Another reason for not including a chapter on these subjects in our initial outline was that we have no magical alternatives to the painstaking and methodical attention to detail which are needed for this part of the study. We can merely record the way we did it and the checks we built into our system. To do it well you need to be obsessional.

Coding

Our questionnaire had 31 pages of questions with 33 blank sheets for recording qualifications and additional comments. In addition there were extra yellow pages if the deceased person had been in more than one hospital during the last twelve months of their life, and additional pink sheets if they had been visited at home by more than one sort of nurse during this time. Most of the questions were precoded, although often with the option of an 'other' answer to be specified. The majority of open questions were designed to be used as illustration, not statistical analysis. They were also used to try and get informants to think about a topic before answering specific questions.

As an intermediary stage between the questionnaire and the computer we used transfer sheets. These contained the column numbers for the computer files, boxes for the codes and the question numbers to which the column number and box related. The codes themselves consisted basically of the precodes on the questionnaire, additional codes for other contingencies (including inadequate data and uncertainties) and precise instructions about the cirumstances in which a code or column was omitted or left blank (for example detailed questions about hospital admissions when the person had not been in hospital). To try and reduce errors we used the same code numbers or symbols for certain contingencies throughout.

A complication of the computer programme SPSS/PC+, which we were using for the first time, was that each question could only have one answer – it did not allow multi-punching or coding on the same column. One of us (AC) found this particularly frustrating as she had used punch cards for most of her research career, and more recently a survey programme SNAP which could cope with multi punching. She felt resentful of the number of columns taken up, and subsequently the amount of paper used, by allocating one column to each possible item in what on a punch card would have been a single column covering up to ten items. For a number of these questions that could have more than one answer we adopted the strategy of using three or four columns to code up to three or four items instead of allowing one column to each possible answer. In spite of allowing more columns than seemed necessary from our test coding this led to us having to make subsequent difficult and arbitrary decisions about which items to code when more than the number allowed for had been indicated at the interview.

To construct the codes one of us drew up a coding frame on the basis of twenty questionnaires, two from each area. Each of us then used this frame to test code 50 questionnaires again drawn from all ten areas. Problems and discrepancies were identified and discussed and the frame modified in the light of this experience.

The rest of the coding was done by two coders each of whom completed a set of transfer sheets for all the questionnaires. The transfer sheets were then compared and any discrepancies identified and listed, usually by the second coder who then corrected any obvious errors and discussed with one of us any differences in interpretation. Both sets of transfer sheets were corrected after these discussions.

We were lucky to have two experienced coders who had worked as coders for the Institute before. They were familiar with our procedures, interested in the topic and to some extent at least identified with the aims and outlook of the Institute. One in particular had worked on a range of Institute surveys over the last ten years. They collected the questionnaires from the Institute, worked in their homes and were paid, like the interviewers, on an hourly basis. This availability of efficient and willing help made this stage of the process relatively easy for us. But it is a stage which demands constant and meticulous attention to detail and there is little or no scope for imaginative creation. It is also a stage which makes the researcher who is involved in it aware of the range and limitations of the data: it reveals the shortcomings of the questionnaire design and the failings of interviewers.

Data entry

We were lucky too in having a professional data entry person, who had worked on other Institute projects, available to help with this phase of the study. She works at great speed – up to 200 depressions a minute – but is still extremely accurate. Even so we asked her to enter the data twice, using the two transfer sheets filled in by the coders. This 'verification' procedure identified discrepancies in either the data entry or ones that had been missed when the coding was compared.

But before the data could be fed into the computer the files had to be set up. As we had a new computer and a programme SPSS/PC + that was new to us we had to learn how to use these. One of us, CS, who had used SPSS on a main frame computer before, was quite keen to do this. So he went through the manual and learnt how to set up the files and how to specify the values acceptable for each variable. He also found out how to make the computer reject answers to questions that should not have been asked, so there was a further check on the accuracy of the interviewing, coding and data entry.

The amount of information we had collected and the different bases to which it related meant that 16 separate files had to be set up. Three covered the basic data about the deceased's life from the main questionnaire, as each file could only contain a maximum of 200 variables. Unfortunately instructions about omitting particular questions cannot be carried over from one file to another. We discovered too late that we should have repeated a few key codes on the three basic files in order to facilitate 'skipping' and 'cleaning.'

The other files related to:

1 the symptoms reported for each person;
2 the hospitals to which they were admitted in the year before they died (details were collected about up to two);
3 different types of nurses who had visited their homes during that time (again details were obtained about no more than two);
4 'open' questions that were not precoded on the questionnaire but classified later on the basis of the answers given;
5 information from the death registration form;

6 data about the people for whom no interview was obtained – reasons for failure and information about the attempts and any facts that could be established;
7 the questionnaire filled in by general practitioners;
8 information from the DHSS and medical directory about all the general practitioners identified;
9 the general questionnaire completed by hospital consultants;
10 the general questionnaire completed by home nurses;
11 the questionnaire about specific patients completed by hospital doctors;
12 the questionnaire about specific patients completed by home nurses;
13 the professionals who did not cooperate.

The codes for each of these variables had also to be labelled – a task entrusted to a more junior member of staff once the way to do it had been mastered by us. Our final role at that stage was to be available to sort out the queries that arose and the discrepancies identified.

Computing

At this stage the complex task of matching the different files had to be mastered – and was particularly involved as we wanted to be able to compare professionals' accounts of hospital or nursing episodes with respondents' accounts from the main questionnaire. To illustrate the complexity: a patient could have been in up to two different hospitals, involving a duplication of his or her serial number in the hospital episodes file. The doctors under whom he or she was admitted could themselves have seen other patients in the sample in that or another hospital. Each hospital episode had to be assigned both a patient serial number and a consultant number, and each interview with a consultant about a hospital episode had to have both serials recorded on the relevant file.

One problem was that we wanted to make some comparison with the earlier, 1969 survey. At the time that study was analysed on punch cards which had been retained at the Institute. But the data had also been deposited with the ESRC data bank and they helpfully provided us with an IBM compatible floppy disc containing the data we wanted to re-analyse. With the help of our Institute statistician, Joy Windsor, we were able to use this. But making comparisons with the earlier study was still a time consuming and finicky job. For example, in the earlier study we had not asked any questions about the care from general practitioners of people who had spent all the last year of their lives in a hospital or any other institution. In 1987, with more people living in residential homes for the elderly and under the care of a general practitioner these questions were asked in those circumstances. So certain categories of patients had to be excluded to make the results from the two studies compatible.

There were other frustrations ahead. In spite of the dual coding, the double entry of data, the definition of acceptable codes and the built in rules about the questions to be answered, the data were not as 'clean' as we had hoped and in the course of our analyses we had sometimes to stop and sort out inconsistencies that were only identified when we cross tabulated certain responses.

At this stage Graham Farrow joined us to help with cleaning the data initially and then to check the various papers and reports from the study. One of the main reasons for inconsistencies in the punched data which he identified was that the situation was sometimes more complicated than our instructions had allowed for and interviewers sometimes asked questions which according to our rules for skipping should have been left out but which applied in that particular instance. We had stressed at the briefing sessions that the instructions about skipping were important because they would prevent people being asked inappropriate questions, but if there was any doubt interviewers should ask questions if they were relevant.

An illustration of this problem was a mentally handicapped young man who had been in a residential home for fifteen years but who went home to his parents at weekends. Our skipping instructions indicated that questions about care at home should be omitted for people in institutions for a year or more, but the interviewer had asked them as they were relevant for this person.

Another reason for inconsistencies which Graham identified was the difficulty of borderline classifications. For instance, several questions about care were omitted for people who had died suddenly with no illness or warning or time for care. Our instructions to interviewers pointed out that people who died from accidents should not necessarily be counted as sudden deaths as the person might have been cared for in hospital before dying. The criterion was whether they were admitted to a ward rather than dying in emergency or the casualty department. But for one person who died only two hours after admission the interviewer had quite reasonably felt that the detailed questions on hospital care did not apply and to make this consistent it was recoded as a sudden death. A further example of a classification problem was a nun who had died in a convent. Our respondent was another nun in the convent who was initially coded as an official of that institution, but she had known the person who died for over thirty years and the interviewer had asked her questions about the impact of the death on her life which were not normally put to officials. In the light of this her relationship to the person who died was recoded as a friend.

In each of these examples our interviewers had responded sensitively to the situation. In two instances they had asked questions that were relevant even though our instructions had indicated that they should be omitted. This was useful for illustrative purposes and for understanding what had happened in the individual cases. Our coders had been reluctant to ignore the relevant data but for statistical consistency the questions had to be recoded. In the other instance the interviewer had decided not to ask questions which seemed irrelevant in that particular situation although they should have been asked according to our guidelines. On consideration we agreed with her and altered our definition for that particular death.

Sometimes we identified apparent discrepancies but when we went back to the questionnaires found that they were reasonable. For instance, some questions were omitted if people had spent all the last year of their lives in hospital or in a residential home. Information about the length of time spent in hospital and in residential homes was recorded at different questions and we found some questions had been omitted when people had spent less than a year in a hospital or home. But when we went back to the questionnaires we found seven people had spent all the last year of their life in some institution, but part of the time in hospital and part of the time in a residential home.

Analysis

Most of our analyses have been straightforward. We have tried to restrict the cross tabulations we do to those we are sure we need and not to do large runs of tabulations 'while we are at it'. But there are some advantages in doing a series of tabulations by the same variable: they can be filed together and more easily found on later occasions; it saves time on the computer, particularly if two files have to be merged; if no unnecessary tabulations are done it also saves paper.

For testing the differences that emerged we have relied almost entirely on chi-squared and t tests, together with the z test of the difference between proportions. These we have done while we are writing to decide on the differences to mention and emphasise. We have used the computer to identify individuals of particular interest or concern and then searched the questionnaires for illuminating and vivid quotations to enlighten and inform our statistics and to stress important findings.

Conclusion

The shortness of this chapter does not reflect the length of time these procedures took. Coding the interviews with relatives was spread over eight months. It started before all the interviewing was done and went on while we were identifying and collecting information from the professionals. The questionnaires from the doctors and nurses were much shorter and straightforward to code. Data entry, thanks to the availability and skill of Hazel Adams, took a relatively short time and could be done in batches while the coding was still going on. Computing and cleaning the data took longer than we had planned largely because of the complexities of the data which in turn stem from the enormous variety of circumstances people encounter in the last year of their lives. Analysis is an ongoing process which will continue as long as we are preparing papers on the project. All four stages demand assiduous attention to detail.

8 How representative are our data?

At last we had collected all our data and got them on to the computer. But before we could start using them we needed to find out how representative they were and to check, as far as we could, their reliability.

This chapter starts by comparing our sample of deaths (excluding the additional hospice ones) with data from national statistics. It then looks at the effect of losing two areas and at any identifiable biases resulting from our failure to interview anyone about some of the deaths in the sample. The second part of the chapter is about the professionals and the biases resulting from some relatives being unwilling for us to approach doctors and our failure to identify all the doctors and nurses who cared for the people in our sample and to persuade all those identified to participate in the study.

Comparisons with national statistics

In Table 5 data from national statistics are compared with information from the death registration forms of three groups:

1 The initial sample relating to the 12 areas selected.
2 The sample in the ten areas in which we tried to interview someone about all the deaths in the sample.
3 The deaths for which someone was interviewed.

The national statistics available relate to deaths in 1986 in England and Wales (OPCS 1989). A comparison of the age distribution of the initial 12 area sample selected showed no significant differences* but the difference between the 10 areas covered and the national distribution was significant at the 5% level largely because the 10-area sample contained a relatively high proportion of deaths among people aged 45–54, and this bias persisted among the deaths for whom an interview was obtained. There was no significant bias in any of the groups in relation to sex, or marital status of women – data about the marital status of men are not given on the non-confidential part of the death registration form. It is also possible to compare the interview data on marital status and sex with information from national statistics. Table 6 shows that the distributions are similar.

---

* In general attention is only drawn to differences which are significant at the 5% level.

Table 5 Comparisons with national statistics for age and sex, and marital status of women

	Study samples			England and Wales 1986
	12 areas selected	10 areas covered	Deaths about which interview obtained	
Age at death	%	%	%	%
15–24	0.9	1.0	0.8	0.8
25–34	0.8	1.0	1.3	0.8
35–44	1.3	1.5	1.6	1.7
45–54	5.9	6.4	6.2	4.0
55–64	12.2	12.6	12.5	12.1
65–74	23.6	23.1	23.0	25.0
75–84	33.9	32.9	31.6	35.4
85 and over	21.4	21.5	23.0	20.2
Sex	%	%	%	%
Male	49.5	48.5	47.1	49.4
Female	50.5	51.5	52.9	50.6
Number of deaths (= 100%)	950*	800	639	572,601
Marital status of women	%	%	%	%
Single	12.9	13.6	13.6	12.3
Married	27.3	27.4	28.4	27.0
Widowed	57.3	56.3	55.0	57.5
Divorced	2.5	2.7	3.0	2.8
Not stated	–	–	–	0.4
Number of deaths (= 100%)	480	412	338	289,709

* 80 in each of eleven areas, 70 in the twelfth.

Information about the place of death and method of certification are compared in Table 7. National statistics on method of certification relate to deaths at all ages. Even so our three samples had similar distributions to the national one. But over place of death it would seem that our samples contain a relatively low proportion of deaths in institutions and a high proportion of deaths in people's own homes. This is probably an effect of the classification which we did from the death registrations forms. On those forms some hospices, nursing homes and homes for the elderly may be just indicated by an address. For example, deaths at St Christopher's hospice are recorded on the death registration forms as occurring at 53 Lawrie Park Road. When the address of the place of death was the same as the deceased's usual address we assumed this was the deceased's home.

Table 6 Comparison of interview data on sex and marital status with national statistics

	Interview data	National statistics 1986
	%	%
Male		
Married	30.7	30.9
Single	4.9	5.0
Widowed	8.5	11.5
Divorced	2.7	1.7
Female		
Married	14.9	13.8
Single	7.9	6.2
Widowed	29.6	29.4
Divorced	0.8	1.5
Number of deaths (= 100%)*	632	567,312

* Marital status was not recorded at 1.1% of the interviews and on 0.9% of the death registrations.

Table 7 Comparison with national statistics of method of certification and place of death

	Study samples			England and Wales 1986*
	12 areas selected	10 areas covered	Deaths about which interview obtained	
Method of certification	%	%	%	%
Medical practitioner	74.7	74.3	74.3	75.7
Coroner with inquest	4.2	4.9	4.5	3.8
Coroner with post-mortem	19.7	19.8	19.9	20.5
Coroner – unspecified	1.4	1.0	1.3	–
Number of deaths	950	800	639	581,203
Place of death coded from registration form	%	%	%	%
Hospital	57.0 ⎫	57.2 ⎫	54.8 ⎫	
Hospice	3.6 ⎬ 64.3	3.8 ⎬ 64.4	3.6 ⎬ 61.9	63.3
Nursing home	3.7 ⎭	3.4 ⎭	3.5 ⎭	
Other institution	0.9	0.5	0.6	6.3
Own home	28.9	28.9	30.5	25.1
Other address	3.9 ⎫	4.1 ⎫	4.7 ⎫	⎫
Dead on arrival at hospital	1.6 ⎬ 5.9	1.6 ⎬ 6.2	1.7 ⎬ 7.0	⎬ 5.3
Elsewhere	0.4 ⎭	0.5 ⎭	0.6 ⎭	⎭
Number of deaths	950	800	639	572,601

* For method of certification these relate to deaths for all ages.

An analysis of our classification from the death registration form with the place of death reported by the relatives and others whom we interviewed showed that 'respondents' reported that 85 of the 639 deaths, 13%, occurred in nursing or old people's homes. Over half, 54%, of these deaths had been classified from the death registration form as occurring in their own homes, 31% in nursing or residential homes 14% at other addresses and 1% in hospital.

A comparison of the interview data on place of death with national statistics showed a better match on own home: 24.4% compared with 25.1%, a reasonable match on all institutional deaths – 67.5% against 69.6% – and rather more of the people we interviewed reporting deaths in other places – 8.1% against 5.3%.

The other comparison that can be made with national statistics relates to the cause of death which had been coded by OPCS on the death registration forms (See Table 8). The distribution for the eleven groups of causes for which numbers were large enough showed no significant differences between our three sample groups and national statistics, even though our samples seemed to contain rather fewer deaths from respiratory diseases and more from injuries or poisonings than might be expected.

To sum up, the comparisons with national statistics have revealed problems in our classification of place of death from the death registration forms and a bias in the ten areas we covered leading to a slight over representation of deaths among people aged 45–54.

The loss of two areas

Comparisons with national statistics can identify major flaws in a sample, but when certain information is available about those who do not respond or were not included in the study for other reasons, a more sensitive indicator of any bias among the failures is an analysis of the response in different groups.

It is possible to use the information from the death registration forms to identify first any bias resulting from the loss of two study areas.

One bias is that the sample of deaths from the two lost areas contained a smaller proportion of deaths of people under 55 than did our sample in the ten areas we covered: 4% compared with 10%. This, as we showed in the last section, led to an over representation of younger deaths in our study. The sample in the two lost areas also had a low proportion of deaths for which the method of certification was a

Table 8 Comparison with national statistics of cause of death

Cause of death	12 areas selected %	10 areas covered %	Deaths about which interview obtained %	England and Wales 1986 aged 15 and over %
I Infectious and parasitic diseases	0.2	0.2	0.3	0.4
II Neoplasms	27.0	27.1	26.3	24.5
III Endocrine, nutritional and metabolic disorders etc.	1.6	1.1	0.9	1.8
IV Diseases of the blood and blood forming organs	0.8	0.9	1.1	0.4
V Mental disorders*	2.9	2.8	2.7	2.2
VI Diseases of the nervous system and sense organs	2.1	2.3	2.2	1.9
VII Diseases of the circulatory system	47.5	47.4	48.8	48.7
VIII Diseases of the respiratory system	8.1	8.4	7.6	10.9
IX Diseases of the digestive system	3.4	2.9	2.7	3.1
X Diseases of genito-urinary system	1.4	1.5	1.7	1.4
XIII Diseases of the musculo-skeletal system and connective tissue	0.6	0.6	0.6	0.9
XVI Signs, symptoms and ill defined conditions	0.2	0.1	0.2	0.4
XVII External causes of injury or poisoning	4.0	4.6	4.7	3.1
Other causes	0.2	0.1	0.2	0.3
Number of deaths (= 100%)	950	800	639	572,601

* For the study sample Alzheimer's disease even without dementia was included here and not under diseases of the nervous system and sense organs.

coroner with inquest: 1% against 5% in the sample in the ten areas, and associated with this for only 1% of the deaths in the two areas was the coroner recorded as the person who informed the registrar of the deaths; it was 5% in the ten areas.

Other data from the death registration form that we could compare for the two groups of areas related to the country in which the deceased person was born, their social class as indicated by their own or their husband's occupation and the month in which the death occurred. There were no significant differences between the two groups of areas on these characteristics.

Both the two lost areas were north of the Bristol-Wash line so 58% of the deaths in the 12 areas were north of this line compared with 50% in the ten areas.

The most important effect of losing two areas that we have identified is an age bias in our sample, giving us a comparatively high proportion of deaths among those aged 45–54.

The deaths for which no interview was obtained

For 20% of the sample of deaths in the ten areas we covered we were unable to find anyone who was willing and able to give us information about the last year of the person's life. The main reason for this was refusal which accounted for 62% of the failures. For 6% no one was identified who knew the person well enough to help, for 11% the person who was identified lived too far away for the interviewer to contact, for 4% the person was temporarily away and for 8% the person's address was not known. A variety of other reasons accounted for the rest.

Response rates in the ten study areas varied from 89% in Hull and 86% in Rochdale and Bradford to 70% in Luton and 69% in Lambeth – a significant difference. As in other studies the response was higher in areas north of the Bristol-Wash line (83%) than in areas south of it (76%).

So while deaths in London and the south are somewhat under represented in our final sample compared with all deaths in the ten areas, this bias somewhat redressed that caused by the lost areas being in the north.

Response rates did not vary with the place of death (hospital or home and so on), the sex of the person who died, nor for women with their marital status. If anything the response was rather greater for deaths of people aged 85 or more, 85% against 78% for those dying at a younger age. There was a suggestion that the response rate might have been lower for those classified as Social Class IV or V; it was 76% for them compared with 82% for those classified as Social Class I, II or III – but this difference did not quite reach the level of statistical significance. Country of birth, cause of death, method of certification and informant of death, were all unrelated to the response rate.

For the deaths for which no interview was obtained, the interviewers tried to collect some information about who the person who died had lived with and about any known relatives. They were able to do this for 91% of the 'failures'. These data are compared in Table 9 with information about the people for whom an interview was obtained.

There was a suggestion that those about whom we were unable to obtain information were more likely to live alone and less likely to have been married at the time of their death – but these differences did not quite reach significance. When someone had been married at the time of their death their spouse would generally be able to give us the information we wanted but may not always have been willing to do so. The response rate to a study of elderly widowed people (Bowling and Cartwright 1982) was rather lower, 74%, than on this study, 80%.

Table 9 The deaths for which no interview was obtained: who the person lived with and their known relatives

	Deaths for which	
	no interview	interview
Lived:	%	%
Alone	35	26
In institution	11	16
With others	54	58
Number of deaths** (= 100%)	133	629
Known relatives:	%	%
None	3	10
Spouse	37	45
Children	65	71
Others/siblings*	23	64
Number of deaths** (= 100%)	147	618

 * This relates to brothers and sisters only for those who were interviewed.
** A few for whom inadequate information was obtained have been omitted from this and subsequent tables.

There was no evidence that those not included in the survey were any more or less likely to have children and the data about other relatives are difficult to interpret. At the interview informants were specifically asked about any brothers or sisters who were alive when the person died, but when an interview was not completed interviewers just recorded any information they were given about any relatives the person they spoke to was aware of. In theory this might include a wider range of people, and possibly did so when there were no other known relatives as the proportion with none was lower among those for whom no interview was obtained. However 'none' among those interviewed indicates only that they were single or widowed and did not have children or siblings.

There is then some suggestion that isolated people may have been less likely to be covered by the study as rather more of those we were unable to obtain an interview about may have lived alone and been unmarried.

The response from professionals

The second phase of the study involved five separate surveys of health professionals. The general practitioners were sent a postal questionnaire asking for their general views; the consultants were sent a similar questionnaire which they could return postally, and they were also asked to give interviews – or to nominate someone on their behalf to be interviewed – about the care of specific patients. The community nurses, like the consultants, were sent a postal questionnaire asking for their general views and were asked for interviews about the care of specific patients.

What follows is an account of how representative these five surveys were of the people involved and the patients they cared for. Sources of bias include difficulties in identifying professionals as well as their non response once identified.

General practitioners

In fourteen cases we did not ask about the general practitioner as the person had been in a hospital for the whole year before death. Two people had no general practitioner and ten respondents did not know whether the person who died had had a general practitioner. For 47 the respondent knew the person had had a general practitioner but could not name the doctor. So for 9% of those at least theoretically under the care of the general practice service we had no doctor's name. For a further 13, 2%, the doctor had died or retired.

Friends, neighbours and relatives outside the immediate family (that is not spouses, children, parents or siblings) were less likely than others to name a general practitioner: 28% of friends and neighbours could not name the doctors and 18% of the relatives outside the immediate family. Six out of the nine coroners did not know anything about general practitioners of the deceased. Spouses, however, were most likely to be able to name the doctor: less than 1% could not, and this proportion was also low, 2%, for staff of institutions.

People for whom a general practitioner was named were more likely to live in households with others (96% for them compared with 83% for those living alone and 86% for those in residential or nursing homes). In addition, the proportion with a named general practitioner was rather higher, 95%, among the middle class than among the working class, 89%. It was 84% among those who could not be classified in this way. (Class was determined by information on the death registration form about the occupation of the person who died or, for married women of their husband. Classes I, II and III non manual have been taken as middle class.) When the cause of death was an injury general practitioners were less often named – 70% compared with 92% for other causes and, related to this, the proportion was low for sudden deaths with no previous illness or warning or time for care – 79% compared with 92% for others. It was also lower for widowed people than others 85% against 95%, but there was no difference between men and women or for people of different ages.

Three-hundred-and-ninety-seven general practitioners were identified and when they were sent a general questionnaire about their views and experiences of caring for people who were dying 245 of them, 62%, replied after two reminders. These were the doctors of 346, 55% of the 625 people who were, at least theoretically, under the care of a general practitioner during the last year of their lives.

When the doctor had been identified by a friend or neighbour of the person who died only 44% responded compared with 58% of others, which suggests that the information may have been less accurate. Other characteristics of the people who died discussed previously and including social class were not related to whether their general practitioner replied or not. Another possibility we considered was whether responding doctors were seen as giving more or less good care than those who did not reply. But there was no difference between the two groups by whether their care was rated excellent, good, fair or poor by respondents, nor in the ratings of how understanding the doctors were seen to have been or whether they were willing or reluctant to visit patients at home. Similar numbers of home visits were reported for the patients of the doctors who replied and those who did not.

However, the general practitioners who replied were different in some ways from those who did not as analysis of data from the DHSS shows. Fifty-seven per cent of doctors born before 1950 responded compared with 76% of those born after this date. Responders were also more likely to have qualified in Great Britain: 64% of these doctors replied, but only 50% of those qualifying in other countries. Trainers were more likely to reply (83% replied as opposed to 58% of non trainers). Doctors in practices with six or more principals were more likely to reply than doctors in smaller partnerships (73% as opposed to 57%). There were no significant differences with their sex, average list size, or whether access to their area for new doctors was restricted or not.

Twenty-two per cent of the responders compared with 15% of those who did not reply were members or fellows of the Royal College of General Practitioners, a difference which might occur by chance but which is in the same direction as that observed on other Institute studies (Cartwright and Smith 1988, Cartwright and Anderson 1981, Cartwright 1967).

Thus, the chief factor determining whether we were successful in finding out the name of the general practitioner was whether we interviewed someone who knew the deceased well. Among the general practitioners who replied, younger doctors who were trained in Great Britain and were trainers were over-represented.

Hospital consultants

Hospital consultants were asked about their general views and experiences of caring for the dying and about the care of specific patients who had spent time in hospital during the last year of their lives. The information we have that can be related to those who did and did not reply comes mainly from our interviews and is about hospital episodes. So the response in relation to these is considered first.

Hospital episodes. A hospital episode was defined for the purpose of the survey as one or more admissions to a single hospital or hospice during the last twelve months of the person's life. We made provision on our questionnaire to relatives and others who knew the deceased for up to two episodes to be described. There were 626 of these. Doctors answered questions about 226 of them: 36%. For 89 (14%) of the episodes a relative was unwilling for us to approach the doctor and for a further 12 (2%) the hospitals involved were unable to identify the doctor. This means that the 226 completed interviews represent a response rate of 43% of the 525 episodes for whom we had consultants' names and permission to approach them.

We more often got an interview about episodes in hospices (92%) than in hospitals (35%). Smaller institutions with less than 300 beds were more likely to be included than larger ones: 45% compared with 32%, and, related to this, hospitals either wholly or partly devoted to acute care were *less* likely to be represented than others (33% as against 55% of others). There was no difference between episodes in private hospitals and others.

The sex, age and social class of the person who died were not associated with whether an interview was gained about a hospital episode. But we got a higher response when the episode culminated in death, 43% compared with 27% of others, and if the person eventually died of cancer, 43% against 33% for episodes relating to people who died from other causes. Interviews were also more likely to be gained when the initial respondent had felt the quality of medical care was 'excellent' as opposed to good, fair or poor (43% of these as opposed to 33% of other ratings) and the same is true of ratings of nursing care (42% against 33%).

These last two differences suggest that the episodes about which we got information from the consultants or other hospital doctors may have been handled rather better than others not included in this part of the study.

General views. Two-hundred-and-ninety-five consultants were identified from our interviews and inquiries to hospitals. A further 28 were identified from the death registration forms of people who died in hospital but for whom we did not get an interview. So 323 were sent postal questionnaires about their general views and experiences as we did not feel it was necessary to have the agreement of relatives to this part of the study. Two-hundred-and-eleven, 65%, replied.

The consultants who returned questionnaires were involved in 52% of the 626 hospital episodes reported in the first part of the study. Doctors who were asked about several patients were not significantly less likely to respond to the general questionnaire.

The biases to this part of the study for the most part were similar to those for the hospital episodes. General questionnaires were more often completed when the episode that led to the identification of the doctor had been in a hospice than a hospital (92% compared with 53%) and when it concerned the place in which the person had died (56% against 47%). But there was no difference with the size and type of hospital, and with cause of death it was not cancer that stood out but circulatory disease. If the patient died of a stroke or heart disease only 47% of consultants replied as opposed to 57% for other causes of death.

Judgments of the quality of nursing care were not related to the response of the consultants but the medical care was more likely to be rated as 'excellent' if the consultant had replied: 60% compared with 51% of the episodes for which the consultant concerned did not reply. So for this part of the study too there is some indication that our data may be biased towards those giving better care.

Community nurses

Like the consultants, community nurses were asked to complete a general questionnaire and ones about specific patients in our sample for whom they had cared. Our data for which we can compare respondents and non-respondents relates to nursing episodes. These were defined as one or more visits from a particular type of nurse to the home (including visits to residential homes). More than one of the same sort of nurse could be involved in an episode but only one nurse was asked about it. Thus a person who was visited by several district nurses and one MacMillan nurse had two nursing episodes.

Out of 639 interviews 280 nursing episodes were recorded, for which nurses were interviewed about 113 (40%). This includes one death for whom the original respondent reported one episode, but the nurse manager we contacted reported two.

It will be recalled that the chief source of difficulty in getting interviews was not the response from individual nurses, but the difficulty in identifying them. Of the 280 episodes reported we were able to identify and approach nurses for only 125 (45%). Of these 113 represents a response rate of 90%. Only 100 nurses were identified but 92 completed general questionnaires. They were involved in 42% of the episodes reported.

Differences in the response rates to both the general questionnaire and to the ones about individual patients are shown in Table 10.

Response rates were high when the person died at home and when the person died of cancer. They were relatively low when the cause of death was ischaemic heart disease. Response rates were relatively high for episodes in which a district nurse was involved, but nurse managers were more often able to identify a nurse in those circumstances (for 52% of those episodes compared with 28% for episodes involving other sorts of nurses). There was also a higher response for episodes involving more care.

Table 10 **Differences in response rates by community nurses to the general questionnaire and to the questionnaires about individual patients**

Nature of episode	Response to general questionnaire	Response to questionnaire about episode	Number of episodes (= 100%)
Place of death			
at home	51%	49%	103
elsewhere	37%	35%	177
Cause of death			
Cancer	53%	50%	130
Ischaemic heart disease	25%	25%	51
Other	36%	34%	99
Age at death			
under 75	49%	46%	133
75 or more	36%	35%	147
Type of nurse			
District	47%	45%	194
Other	30%	28%	83
Frequency of attendance			
More than once a week	51%	48%	154
Less often	32%	30%	110
Length of attendance			
Less than week	23%	20%	35
A week or longer	46%	43%	235
All episodes	42%	40%	280

Judgments by relatives and others of the quality of care provided by the nurses were not associated with the completion of either type of questionnaire. So there was no evidence that nurses providing better care were more likely to participate in the study than others. The biases that have been identified relate more to the nature of the patients' problems, towards those dying of cancer, those dying when they were comparatively young, those dying at home and those receiving more frequent and more long term nursing care.

Summary

In contrast to the earlier, 1969, study comparisons with national statistics revealed no major biases. There was a slight over-representation of deaths among people aged 45–54 which was attributable to the loss of two study areas. Failure to interview someone about all the sample of deaths in the remaining areas resulted in some bias between areas and possibly an under representation of those who lived alone and were not married: the isolated.

The response from general practitioners, 62%, compares poorly with the 1969 survey of *Life before death* (Cartwright, Hockey and Anderson 1973) when 79% replied to either a postal questionnaire (fourth-fifths) or an interview (one-fifth). People less close to the deceased who, presumably, knew less about the person's affairs, were less likely to be able to name a general practitioner.

Among the general practitioners who were identified the main biases in their response rates related not to the characteristics and circumstances of the patients but to attributes of the doctors themselves. Younger doctors, those trained in Britain, those in larger partnerships and trainers were more likely to reply.

We were able to identify most of the hospital consultants, but disappointingly few of the nurses. However, the response rate from nurses, once approached, was much higher than that for consultants. District nurses were easier for managers to identify, and the replies are therefore biased towards this type of nurse. People who died at home and those dying from cancer were over-represented in the response from nurses as were those receiving more care. The response from consultants is skewed in a number of important respects, there being a tendency for cancer patients, episodes of terminal care or care resulting in death, and hospice episodes to be over-represented. The observation that the most helpful doctors, from our point of view, tended also to be the ones covering episodes where respondents judged medical and nursing care to be 'excellent', suggest that the best (or nicest) doctors are the ones who help in social surveys!

9 How good are our data?

In addition to the response rates and the various biases that were identified in the last chapter, there are three other indicators of the quality of our data which are looked at in this chapter: comparisons of the interview data with information from the death registration forms; variations in responses with the different types of respondents, and congruity between interviews with relatives and the information given to us by hospital doctors and community nurses about individual patients.

In this chapter we also report a separate exercise in which we aimed to compare reports of relatives interviewed some weeks after a death with data from interviews with patients dying of cancer.

Comparisons between interview and death registration data

Two factors can be compared: the place of death and the cause of death. (The sex and age of the person who died were given to the interviewer before they approached anyone for an interview.)

Place of death. We classified the information from the death registration form separately and independently from the information obtained at interview. Table 11 shows the information from the two sources tallied for 83% of the deaths. The main discrepancies were that for 47, 7%, an address was recorded on the death registration form which was the same as the usual address of the person who died. There was no indication that it was a residential home. At the interview it was found to be a residential or nursing home where the person had lived for some time before he or she died. Presumably local Office of Population Censuses and Surveys employees have this information when classifying the place of death for OPCS returns and statistics. Similar explanations account for the 13, 2%, classified as 'other address' from the death registration form but turning out at the interview to be a nursing or residential home where the person had recently been admitted. The 13, 2%, for which 'hospital' was recorded on the death registration form and 'street' at the interview were either sudden deaths with no previous illness or deaths from heart attack with some earlier illness or warning. For all of them the precise place of death was uncertain as it was for three reported at interview as dying at home but on the death registration form as 'dead on arrival at hospital'.

Table 11 Place of death from interview and death registration

Interview	Hospital	Hospice	Death registration form Other institution	Own home	Other address	DOA at hospital	Other	TOTAL
Hospital	319					1		320
Hospice	–	23						23
Nursing home or other institution	1		26	47	13			87
Own home	8			144	1	3		156
Other person's home	3			1	10			14
Street	13			1		6	2	22
Other	6			2	6	1	2	17
TOTAL	350	23	26	195	30	11	4	639

Similarly, all six deaths recorded on the death registration form as being in hospital but at interview as happening in 'other places' were sudden deaths: five were heart attacks and our informants reported that one happened suddenly at work, one in a hotel foyer, one in a shop, one in a van and one on a boat; the other was a suicide who threw himself off a balcony.

Seven of the eight deaths reported at interview as happening at home but recorded on the death registration form as occurring in hospital were due to heart attack. The attack happened at home and our informant told us the person died there but presumably the body was taken to hospital and that led to the record on the registration form. The widow of one of the people this happened to told us:

> He had taken the dogs for a walk, came back and collapsed at the back door. I phoned the ambulance and made him comfortable. He was unconscious. I waited ten minutes and rang again. They arrived half an hour later but he was dead. I knew he was dead as the ambulance didn't rush.

The friend and neighbour of another person said:

> The night before she was as right as rain, then she was found on the floor at lunch time the next day.

The other death in this group was due to a brain haemorrhage:

> We were in the greenhouse and she just stopped talking to me and dropped on the floor. (Widower)

Three other people who died of heart problems were reported at interview as having died at a relative's home or in a house where the person was working as a builder but on the death registration form as dying in hospital.

The final discrepancy over deaths recorded on the registration form as occurring in hospital related to a man who, according to the death registration form, died of pneumonia. The deputy matron of the old persons' home where he had been living for over two years did not recall what he had died of. She said they had no records and she reported that he died at the home. The most likely explanation would seem to be that her memory was faulty.

Cause of death. At the interview respondents were asked about the person's death and whether he or she had been ill for some time before he/she died. After that they were asked what the person died of. The first or clearly indicated cause of death* was then classified in the broad groups of the International Classification of Diseases and Causes of Death (World Health Organization 1978) with some minor modifications. This is compared with the main or underlying cause of death coded from the death registration data by OPCS in Table 12. The cause of death could not be classified for 6% of the interviews. Among the others, there was agreement between the two sources in 79%. There was least disagreement over cancer deaths. When this was the main cause of death on the registration form it was recorded at the interview for 96%. The main discrepancies and confusions arose between respiratory and circulatory conditions: switches between these two accounted for just over a quarter of the discrepancies. One in eight arose because our respondents reported that the person died of old age and this was only recorded as the main cause of death on one registration form. When mental disorders were recorded as the main cause of death on the registration form the interview respondents were more likely to report a respiratory condition. The eight deaths for which this happened were all of people who, according to the death registration form, suffered from dementia and developed bronchopneumonia. Dementia was classified as the main cause of death.

The deaths attributed to accident or injury on the death registration form but ascribed to respiratory conditions by our respondents seemed puzzling initially, but the injury had led to bronchopneumonia which was recorded first on the death registration form

* Cancer took precedence over other causes.

Table 12 Main cause of death from death registration and interview

Interview	Neoplasm	Circulatory	Respiratory	Digestive	Genitourinary	Injury	Old age	Mental disorders	Alzheimer's	Other nervous systems and sense organs	Other	TOTAL
						Death registration form						
Neoplasm	157	8	–	1	1						1	168
Circulatory	1	232	7		1	3	1	2			4	251
Respiratory	3	26	35		1	4		8		5	6	88
Digestive		1		8								9
Genitourinary		5	1	1	5						1	13
Injury		1				23					1	25
Old age (not senility)	1	11	3	1							1	17
Mental disorders (including senility)								1				1
Alzheimer's, senile dementia		3						3				6
Other nervous systems and sense organs		1								8		9
Other	2	3	1	1					1		6	14
Not classified	4	21	2	5	3			1	1	1		38
TOTAL	168	312	49	17	11	30	1	15	2	14	20	639

and many informants tended to repeat the causes on the form in the order given. For example, for one man this was recorded: 'broncho-pneumonia due to cerebral ischaemia following hanging – killed himself.' Our informant answered our question about the cause of death in precisely these terms but had previously explained that the person who died had been mentally ill for 15 years with schizophrenia.

As circulatory diseases accounted for the largest number of deaths these were broken down into ischaemic heart disease, cerebrovascular accidents (stroke) and other causes. The agreement over these is shown in Table 13.

Table 13   Deaths from circulatory diseases from death registration and interview

| | Death registration form | | |
Interview	Ischaemic heart disease	Cerebrovascular accidents	Other circulatory
Heart attack/angina	115	5	13
Stroke	1	49	3
Other circulatory	30	3	13
Othe causes	18	26	15
TOTAL	164	83	44

Deaths from cerebrovascular accidents according to the death registration form were more often ascribed to a cause other than circulatory disease by our respondents than were deaths from ischaemic heart attacks. Of the 83 deaths ascribed to stroke on the registration forms and classified by respondents 18% were said to be caused by respiratory disease, 5% by old age and 4% by Alzheimer's or senile dementia.

When data from two different sources differ it is often uncertain which is right. For place of death the concept of a right or wrong classification seems reasonable – although for deaths from heart attack it may often be uncertain precisely when or where death occurred. But it would seem that a number of the deaths recorded on registration forms – and therefore included in official statistics – as occurring in hospital may have happened elsewhere. The proportion of 'hospital' deaths in which this happened may be as high as 9% if our informants are accepted as reliable. From some of their reports it is unclear to us why the category 'dead on arrival' was not used more often.

For distinguishing residential homes from ordinary ones local knowledge is needed to classify the information on the death registration form. Our interview data indicated that 8% of deaths occurred in old peoples' homes, which is not significantly higher than 6% of deaths occurring in 'other institutions' according to national statistics. It would have been interesting to compare our interview data with OPCS coding of place of death for the people in our sample, but these data were not available.

For cause of death the OPCS coding was given and as this is done by people experienced in ICD classification it seems appropriate to accept this as the bench mark against which to compare our classification based on interview data and coded by just taking the first cause mentioned – or cancer if it was mentioned at all. For the 94% of deaths for which we were able to classify the cause, agreement was generally good and most discrepancies reflected the fact that most people who die are old and many suffer from more than one condition which contributes to their death.

Data from different types of respondents

We tried to interview the person who could tell us the most about the dead person's last year of life. How successful were we?

At the end of the interview, when they had found out a great deal about the circumstances of the person who died, interviewers were asked to assess whether the person they had seen was the most appropriate person to tell us about the last year of the dead person's life. For 86%, interviewers felt they had seen the best person, for 5% they felt someone else, who was either unwilling or inaccessible, would have been more appropriate, and for 9% they were uncertain. Their assessments depended not only on the appropriateness of the respondent but also on the existence of other people. Thus for three of the nine interviews done with a coroner, environmental health officer or mortuary attendant there was no other more appropriate person.★

The person who informed the registrar of the death was frequently the person we interviewed. They had the same relationship to the deceased for over half, 57%, the deaths. The main difference was that whereas we interviewed the widow or widower about over a

★ Six of these nine interviews were with a coroner, two with an environmental health officer and one with a mortuary attendant. Subsequently they are referred to as interviews with coroners.

third, 36%, of the deaths, he or she was the person who informed the registrar about only a fifth, 20%. In two-fifths of those deaths for which we interviewed the husband or wife, it was a son or daughter who informed the registrar of the death; the reverse only happened for 4% of the deaths for which we interviewed a son or daughter. Clearly informing the registrar is a duty that sons and daughters often take on rather than their widowed parents. But sons and daughters may come from some distance to the place where their mother or father died and not be available some time later. In 12% of the deaths registered by a child or child-in-law we did not interview a relative but either a friend, neighbour or an official. This also happened for 85% of the deaths for which the qualification of the informant on the death registration form was given as 'causing the body to be buried or cremated' and for 55% of those for which it was the coroner.

The respondents most often assessed as appropriate were husbands or wives, 98%, sons or daughters, 91%, brothers or sisters, 83%. Children or siblings in-law were less likely to be felt to have been the best people to see: for only 42% of the interviews with them was this assessment made, but for other relatives the proportion was 88%. Three-quarters of friends who were seen were thought to be most appropriate, half the neighbours and three-quarters of the staff in residential homes.

People who were married at the time of their death were more likely to have had appropriate informants, 89% compared with 83% for those who were single or widowed. But this proportion did not vary significantly with either the sex or the age of the person who died.

Even if they were the most appropriate person available some informants may not have known much about the circumstances or been so aware of the problems and needs of the person who died as others. Before looking at this we need to see how the characteristics of people who died varied with the type of respondent. One indication of respondent's knowledge of people's circumstances might be whether they were present at the person's death: this proportion was 51% for husbands or wives, 28% for sons or daughters, 24% for other relatives, 11% for friends and neighbours and 11% for staff.

The variation in the type of respondent with the marital status of the person who died is shown in Table 14. Wives or husbands were the usual respondent for people who had been married at the time, sons and daughters for the widowed. For the single, respondents were roughly evenly divided between brothers or sisters, other relatives, friends or neighbours and staff of homes.

Table 14 Type of respondent and marital status of person who died

	Married	Single	Widowed, divorced separated
	%	%	%
Husband or wife	79	–	1*
Son or daughter	12	1	48
Brother or sister	–	25	3
Other relative	5	28	17
Neighbour or friend	3	20	15
Staff of home	–	25	15
Coroner etc.	1	1	1
Number of deaths (= 100%)	288	81	263

* Two common law wives responded about men whose first wife had died.

Wives responded for 53% of the men who died, husbands for 21% of the women – a reflection of their different age and marital status. Sons and daughters were the most usual informant for women: 34% compared with 16% for men.

Circumstances and the type of respondent were often related. Seventy seven per cent of those for whom the respondent was a friend or neighbour lived alone compared with 46% of those for whom it was a son or daughter, none if it was a husband or wife and 50% if it was another relative. The relationship between the type of respondent and whether the person who died had any living children and brothers or sisters is shown in Table 15. The proportion with living children was small among those for whom other relatives were interviewed – because sons and daughters were generally preferred as respondents to other relatives. The absence of living children may make it more likely that people will live in residential homes, which may contribute to this proportion being low when the respondent was on the staff of a home. There is also the possibility that some informants may not know about all the deceased person's relatives. This may be partly why the proportion reported to have living siblings was so low when the respondent was a staff member of a home. But as people get older their siblings are more likely to die before them and the nature of the respondent also varied with the age of the person who died.

The older the person the more likely we were to interview a son or daughter and, apart from those under 45, less likely to interview a husband or wife. But the former did not entirely compensate for the latter and for older people we more often had to rely on information from staff in residential homes. The data are in Table 16.

Table 15 The proportion with living children and living siblings reported by different types of informants

	Proportion with		
Respondent	Living children	Living siblings	Number of deaths* (= 100%)
Husband or wife	86%	73%	231
Son or daughter	100%	64%	165
Other relatives	28%	68%	107
Friend or neighbour	44%	52%	67
Staff of home	45%	31%	60
All deaths	71%	64%	639

* Deaths for whom the respondent was a coroner have been excluded from the body of the table. Those for whom inadequate replies were given are included in the total but have been excluded from this and other tables when calculating percentages.

Associated with this variation with age, we more often interviewed a husband or wife when the person died of cancer – 53% compared with 30% for deaths from other causes. And husbands or wives were more often interviewed when the person died at home than in a hospital (48% compared with 37%) and most often when the death occurred in a hospice – 65%.

Table 16 Types of respondents and age of person who died

	Age of person who died					
	Under 45	45–54	55–64	65–74	75–84	85 +
	%	%	%	%	%	%
Husband or wife	44 ⎱48	59 ⎱72	54 ⎱69	58 ⎱76	30 ⎱62	6 ⎱45
Son or daughter	4 ⎰	13 ⎰	15 ⎰	18 ⎰	32 ⎰	39 ⎰
Other relative	39	18	15	13	15	20
Neighbour or friend	9	5	7	9	12	12
Staff of home	–	–	5	2	10	23
Coroner	4	5	4	–	1	–
Number of deaths (= 100%)	23	39	80	147	203	147

Looking at the symptoms reported for the person who died during the last twelve months of life and including any while in a hospital or hospice, coroners and other officials of that nature were unable to answer questions about these and the average number of 'don't knows' or inadequate responses for the 23 symptoms asked about was .01 for husbands or wives, .03 for sons or daughters, .05 for other relatives, .13 for friends or neighbours and .03 for staff of homes. Husbands and wives were most likely to say they did not know about a dry mouth or thirst and dizziness; sons and daughters, other relatives and friends or neighbours, about constipation, and the staff of homes about a dry mouth or thirst.

The symptoms reported by the different types of informants are shown in Table 17. Those who did not know about a particular symptom have been excluded when calculating the percentages and averages. Friends or neighbours reported the fewest symptoms, and as they were reporting about a group of average age this is almost certainly because they were aware of fewer problems. Sons and daughters reported more symptoms than husbands or wives. For many symptoms such as mental confusion and incontinence this is at least partly explained by the different ages of the people they were reporting about: 35% of those for whom sons or daughters were interviewed were 85 or more at the time of their death, 4% of those for whom husbands or wives were seen and 55% for whom the staff of a home reported.

Further analyses by age showed that among those aged 65–74 sleeplessness was reported more often by sons and daughters (for 71%) than by husbands and wives (for 35%), but this may be because sons and daughters more often reported for elderly widowed people and sleeplessness is common after bereavement (Bowling and Cartwright 1982, p98). Differing circumstances may also account for the higher proportion of people aged 75–84 who were reported by staff of homes to suffer from depression: 61% compared with 36% of those for whom spouses or children answered our questions. Some people may feel depressed initially when admitted to a home. There was a similar difference for the same groups in the proportion reported as being bad tempered – 55% compared with 22%. This may be associated with their depression but the variations could arise because of different perceptions of staff in homes and close relatives.

The low proportion of bedsores reported by staff members compared with sons and daughters could be the result of better care in residential homes. But staff of homes do appear to have a relatively optimistic view of things: they were the respondents least likely to describe the quality of life of the people they were asked about as

Table 17 Symptoms reported by different types of respondents

	Husband or wife %	Son or daughter %	Respondent Other relative %	Friend or neighbour %	Staff of home %	All respondents %
Pain	74	74	67	70	69	72
Trouble breathing	44	56	52	49	42	49
Vomiting, feeling sick	30	41	31	31	29	33
Drowsiness	43	57	39	33	34	44
Sleeplessness	37	50	38	34	35	40
Dry mouth/thirst	33	35	34	31	25	33
Mental confusion	29	51	28	27	56	37
Depression	33	42	31	36	46	36
Loss of appetite	46	50	42	45	53	47
Difficulty swallowing	23	30	20	15	15	23
Constipation	34	42	35	34	32	36
Persistent cough	19	26	22	26	8	21
Dizziness	23	44	28	21	29	30
Dribbling	9	22	9	7	18	13
Bad temper	21	22	22	13	42	23
Bed sores	17	29	13	9	8	18
Loss of bladder control	27	47	28	22	46	34
Loss of bowel control	18	30	17	17	33	23
Unpleasant smell	11	18	13	17	13	14
Difficulty seeing	17	36	25	16	27	24
Difficulty hearing	14	48	30	16	40	28
Backache	30	41	23	25	24	31
Other	32	32	40	28	44	34
Average number reported	6.6	9.2	6.9	6.2	7.7	7.4
Number of respondents (= 100%)	231	165	107	67	60	630*

*Excludes the nine coroners, environmental health officers and the mortuary attendant who gave some information but did not answer these questions.

'poor' during the year before they died – only 14% compared with 30% of people assessed by other informants. (People who died suddenly with no illness or warning or time for care were not assessed in this way). However, when asked: 'Looking back now and taking _____'s illness into account do you think he/she died at the best time or would it have been better if he/she had died earlier or later?' the replies of staff of homes had a similar distribution to those of other informants taken together; it was sons and daughters who differed from the others in their views over this: 31% of them thought it would have been better if the person had died earlier compared with 19% of other informants.

The knowledge and assessments of the general practitioner care given to the people who died by different types of respondents are shown in Table 18.

Friends and neighbours were least able to estimate the number of home visits or to know the deceased person's general practitioner. Nearly all the staff of homes knew the person's doctor and could estimate the number of visits. They were the ones who were least critical of general practitioners and the way they looked after the person who died. Sons and daughters tended to be the most critical. Friends and neighbours were comparatively critical of general practitioners about home visiting. It may be that they underestimated the number of visits that had been made, but they were often describing the care given to people who lived alone who may be felt to be in particular need of home visits and at the same time may not request them.

It is difficult to assess the effect of obtaining information from different types of respondents because of the variations in the circumstances they were reporting about. In trying to get as complete a picture as possible about all the people in the sample we had to rely sometimes on information from respondents who may not have been aware of all the relevant circumstances during the last year of the person's life. And some respondents may have guessed at the answers to some questions when they were uncertain or assumed a knowledge they did not have. In general the answers from different types of respondents do not differ all that widely and the variations that have emerged for the most part seem understandable in terms of the characteristics and situation of the people they were telling us about. But we recognise that we have something of a vested interest in interpreting the differences in that way. However, there did seem to be a tendency for sons and daughters to view things in a somewhat gloomy light while the staff of homes seemed inclined to put a more

Table 18 Knowledge and assessments of general practitioner care by different types of respondents

	Husband or wife	Son or daughter	*Respondent* Other relative	Friend or neighbour	Staff of home	All
Not able to estimate number of home visits	0%	13%	12%	28%	9%	9%
Estimated number of home visits during year	6.1	7.6	6.5	4.4	10.6	6.8
Felt deceased person's GP was:	%	%	%	%	%	%
Willing to do home visits	84	78	80	88	93	83
Rather reluctant	14	19	13	12	5	14
Other comment	2	3	7	–	2	3
Felt it would have been helpful if GP had visited deceased more often at home	16%	30%	22%	29%	5%	21%
Described the way the GP looked after the deceased as:	%	%	%	%	%	%
Very understanding	63	58	65	61	77	63
Fairly understanding	20	22	23	16	18	20
Not very understanding	8	9	5	9	5	8
Other comment	9	11	7	14	–	9
Assessed deceased person's care from GP in last year as:	%	%	%	%	%	%
Excellent	41	36	33	32	50	41
Good	31	31	38	33	43	33
Fair	11	20	9	15	5	13
Poor	8	8	6	9	2	7
No care from GP	7	3	3	9	–	5
Other comment	2	2	–	2	–	1
Knew general practitioner or had same one	95%	74%	61%	42%	90%	78%
Thought GP was not an easy person to talk to**	11%	15%	8%	8%	4%	10%
Did not feel GP had time to discuss things**	14%	22%	13%	4%	6%	14%
Number of respondents (= 100%)*	229	160	103	65	59	616

** Those who gave inadequate responses are included in the total but have been excluded when calculating percentages. The 14 who were in hospital all year have been excluded from the table.
** Only asked if respondent knew doctor.

rosy interpretation on situations.

Congruity over hospital care

For 226 reported episodes of hospital admission we have data from both relatives or others and hospital doctors. How good is the agreement between them? Table 19 shows the concordance over the number of times the person who died was said to be admitted to the specific hospital during the year before he or she died.

Table 19 Agreement over number of admissions to particular hospital

Hospital doctor	Relative or other respondent						
	1	2	3	4	5+	More than once*	TOTAL
1	137	4	3				144
2	18	14	3	4		1	40
3	5	3	5		1	2	16
4		1	1	1	2		5
5+	1	2			3	1	7
More than once*	2		1				3
TOTAL	163	24	13	5	6	4	215

* No other information given.

For eleven people one or other of our informants did not answer this question. Among the others there was agreement over three-quarters, 75%, with a further 2% agreeing they were admitted more than once but not specifying the number of times. For 8% the relative reported more admissions than the hospital doctor, whereas in 15% the hospital doctor reported more.

Some illustrations of instances for which the relative reported more are given first.

A daughter had shared the care of her mentally disturbed mother with her sister. They also had a brother still at home who suffered from schizophrenia and needed looking after as well. 'I contacted welfare about my brother and they promised to come to see him and my mother but it took ages. We began to despair of help and it really got us down. She was taken into hospital three times in the last year to give us some relief.' The consultant reported just one admission.

A son had looked after his father who had a series of strokes. He was also a diabetic and suffered from senile dementia. He reported three admissions 'because of his strokes and his blood pressure was rather high and his sugar level was wrong.' The consultant reported a single admission.

Examples of instances where the hospital doctor reported more admissions than the relative are:

A son reported that his mother had been admitted to hospital twice, with three months between the two visits. He said she was in overnight on one occasion and for two nights on the other. His mother had lived with him and his wife and daughter. The consultant reported four admissions in the last 12 months. Both the consultant and the son said the last discharge was six months before death.

A widow said her husband was admitted to hospital twice in the last year of his life. 'He went in for bleeding for a week, then discharged. Then five days later he was admitted for the last time.' She said he'd had a stroke two years before his death and then another a year later, after which he deteriorated. The consultant reported four admissions.

Another widow reported a single admission to one hospital (and three to another). She said he had been in the first hospital for ten days but the doctor there reported a total of five admissions, with a total time of between one and three months.

One of the problems about collecting information from two different sources is that it is often unclear which source is most reliable. Here we have the problem of a defined period – twelve months before the death, whereas both relatives and hospital doctors may include admissions outside that period but during the last illness. They may also forget or omit to tell us about all the episodes during those last twelve months. Both hospital records and relatives' memories are fallible and it seems impossible to tell which is most likely to be correct. The data suggest that between a third and a quarter of the hospitals to which people were admitted in the last twelve months of their lives, discharged and then re-admitted them at least once.

Information about whether or not the person had an operation while he or she was in that hospital during the twelve months before he or she died was also available from both sources for 215 episodes. There was agreement in 88% of instances – and the mean square contingency (a measure of agreement based on the chi-squared statistic for the observed frequencies divided by the number in the sample and ranging from zero to one with a value of 1.0 indicating complete agreement) was 0.41. A rather similar pattern was found for blood transfusion.

Table 20 Agreement over various treatments and procedures

	Reported by						Proportion unknown or not answered by	
	Both	Neither	Relative etc only	Doctor only	Number for which both available (= 100%)	MSC	Relative etc	Doctor
Operation	15%	73%	4%	9%	215	0.41	2%	2%
Physiotherapy	18%	47%	6%	29%	175	0.10	15%	8%
Occupational therapy	3%	81%	3%	13%	181	0.06	15%	6%
Blood transfusion	8%	82%	4%	6%	180	0.34	16%	5%
Chemotherapy	3%	88%	3%	6%	185	0.16	14%	4%
Drip feeding	15%	62%	18%	5%	182	0.20	16%	4%

Agreement over other types of treatment – physiotherapy, occupational therapy, chemotherapy and drip feeding, shown in Table 20, was much less good and there were also substantial proportions of relatives or other informal respondents who could not answer these questions. The inevitable conclusion is that our respondents were often not aware when these procedures had been carried out. There were also a small proportion of instances in which procedures were reported by relatives or others but not by hospital doctors, which suggests that these procedures were not always recorded in the notes. The proportion reported by relatives only was comparatively high for drip feeding, but relatives may not always have understood the purpose of tubes connected to patients.

Over subjective issues like the success of the treatment of pain there was some agreement even though agreement over the presence and treatment of pain was poor. When information was available from both sources, relatives or others reported that the person had been in pain in 65% of hospital episodes, the doctor that the person had received treatment for pain in 71%, but the mean square contingency was only 0.06. However, the treatment might have been so successful that the person did not have pain. When both relative and doctor reported treatment for pain the doctors were more likely to regard the treatment as satisfactory when the relatives reckoned it relieved the pain completely than when they thought it only did so partially or not at all. The trend is in Table 21.

Table 21 Relatives' and hospital doctors' assessments of pain relief

	Relatives' assessment that treatment relieved pain:		
Hospital doctor assessed pain as being:	Completely all the time	Completely some of the time	Partially or not at all
	%	%	%
Satisfactorily controlled	94	88	75
Not satisfactorily controlled	–	8	25
Other comment	6	4	–
Number of episodes (= 100%)	17	26	20

But in spite of the significant association the doctors still regarded the pain as being satisfactorily controlled for three-quarters of the patients whose relatives felt the treatment relieved the pain only partially or not at all.

There was also some concordance, shown in Table 22, over their assessments of the room where the person died or spent most of his or her time in hospital, as being peaceful and quiet.

Table 22 Relatives' and hospital doctors' assessments of the patient's room

	Relatives' assessment		
Hospital doctors' assessment	Very	Fairly	Not at all
	peaceful and quiet		
	%	%	%
Very ⎤ peaceful	23	8	9
Fairly ⎬ and	58	51	35
Not at all ⎦ quiet	18	34	56
Other comment	1	7	–
Number of episodes (= 100%)	79	86	23

Doctors were less likely than relatives to regard the patient's room as very peaceful and quiet. Only 16% of them made such an assessment compared with 42% of relatives.

Table 23 Congruity between nurses and relatives over the number of nurses of a specific type who visited during the last year

| | Relative or other respondent | | | | |
	One	Two–four	Five or more	More than one*	TOTAL
Nurse					
One	12	5	1	–	18
Two–four	22	31	6	3	62
Five or more	3	9	6	3	21
More than one*	1	2	–	–	3
TOTAL	38	47	13	6	104

* No more information available.

Congruity over home nursing

Relatives and others may not always have been aware of what happened to people while they were in hospital but we expected greater congruity between their reports and that of community nurses over home nursing care. This did not happen. Over the number of nurses of a specific type (community nurse, nurse from hospice and so on) who had visited in the last year there was agreement within the broad groups in only just under half the instances or 55% if those agreeing that more than one nurse came are included (see Table 23).

Checking back over individual discrepancies revealed a number of possible reasons for differences:

The nurses did not have access to their notes. This seemed the most probable explanation when husbands or wives reported that more than one nurse had visited but the nurse only reported one.

A different interpretation over the type of nurse. One community nurse was an SEN and apparently thought the type of nurse referred to the grade so only reported visits by herself. The husband reported visits by three district nurses – 'The first two were smashing, the last one was a bit fussy.'

Incomplete information from relatives who had not lived with the person who died. A daughter who had not lived with her mother reported care from one nurse whereas the nurse said that five or more nurses had visited. Both agreed that care had been given for between one and three months.

Different perceptions of care given to people in residential homes. For people living in residential homes it sometimes seemed that nurses tended to include all visits to the home when there may have been some general supervision, whereas the staff who answered our questions reported the care given to the particular patients. On other occasions the records of the two informants did not tally. One nurse who did not have her notes, said over five nurses had visited during a period of a year and they had given massage or exercises, enemas, temperature taking, personal care and helped with lifting and getting in and out of bed. A staff member of the institution, where the person who died had lived for five or more years, said one nurse had cared for the deceased for between a week and a month and helped with bandaging.

In another instance a nurse who had records reported five or more nurses visiting the home regularly once a week for a year or more and caring for the person who died by giving her injections, dressing and 'a blood test as requested by the G.P.' The staff member reported that one nurse had visited for between a week and a month for dressing after the person who died had fallen and hurt her leg.

In addition the follow-up identified one person who had had care from two different sorts of nurses but the reports of relatives and nurses had been incorrectly matched. This was corrected and the discrepancies are not included in the table.

Congruity over the types of care given by the nurses, shown in Table 24, was poor. And the implication is that the data about these from both sources must be regarded with scepticism. It is not possible to apportion the blame for this to incomplete or absent records, poor memories, lack of knowledge or imprecise definitions and questions. All are suspect. Even in relation to night care, which was defined as being between 8 pm and 8 am, agreement was poor and over this and most other activities the nurses reported more than the relatives or others recalled.

Finally, relatives and others were asked whether when the nurse(s) came she (they) had enough time to do things or whether she (they)

Table 24 Congruity over different types of care reported by nurses and by relatives or others

	Reported by				Number	MSC
	Both	Neither	Relative or other only	Nurse only		
Injections	12%	67%	9%	12%	105	0.17
Dressings	27%	43%	17%	13%	107	0.15
Giving medicines	3%	63%	15%	19%	106	0.00
Massaging, exercises	6%	63%	8%	23%	104	0.01
Giving enema	12%	70%	6%	12%	101	0.22
Taking temperature	7%	55%	20%	18%	98	0.00
Help with:						
Bathing	27%	45%	7%	21%	107	0.20
Dressing/undressing	18%	56%	5%	21%	106	0.18
Getting to toilet	11%	61%	7%	21%	104	0.09
Personal care with hair, teeth, shaving	14%	50%	12%	24%	107	0.03
Feeding	0%	89%	4%	7%	105	0.00
Cutting toe nails	4%	77%	7%	12%	103	0.03
Giving a bed pan or bottle	8%	72%	9%	11%	105	0.10
Lifting	25%	41%	7%	27%	106	0.13
Getting in or out of bed	23%	40%	10%	27%	105	0.07
Care at night	5%	63%	4%	29%	107	0.02

hurried over them. Seventy-five per cent thought the nurse(s) had enough time, 18% that she (they) hurried and 7% made other comments. The nurses were asked whether, when they visited particular patients they felt they had enough time to do the things they needed to always (74% felt this); sometimes (22%) or never (4%). Analysis showed these two assessments were not related.

An attempt at validation

In this study and in the earlier, 1969, one, we were concerned that we did not know what the dying people themselves had thought about the care they had been given. Some evidence about discrepancies between patients' and relatives' accounts exists in the literature. Magaziner et al (1988) report that in a study of 361 elderly patients with hip fracture, proxy respondents (that is their relatives interviewed separately and concurrently) overestimated the level of disability and dependency compared to patients' own reports. McCusker and Stoddard (1984), however, report good congruence in a study of 66 chronically or terminally ill patients and their proxies in their answers to the Sickness Impact Profile. However, these studies involved interviews done concurrently, and were not exclusively about people who were dying.

A topic of concern on our main study was the awareness of both patients and relatives that the patient was likely to die. Hinton (1979, 1980 and 1981) studied 80 married people who had cancer and were expected to die within three months. He found a greater awareness of approaching death among patients than their spouses realised. Ahmedzai and his colleagues (1988) report a difference in the opposite direction. In their study, 55% of 40 terminal cancer patients reported awareness to the interviewer, whereas 82% of relatives reported such awareness in patients. This last study also found that relatives reported a higher incidence of physical symptoms than did patients and a lower incidence of anxiety and depression. Morris et al (1986) support part of Ahmedzai's finding, as they report relatives as more likely to say patients were in pain than were patients themselves. Both of these last two studies report low associations between the two sources.

What are the implications of these findings for our study, which relied exclusively on accounts from relatives, friends and others? The data in these previous studies relate to disability, the impact of illness and awareness of dying. In our study we asked about many more things and one of our main concerns was the quality of care.

In an attempt to see how items on our questionnaire, answered by relatives and others who knew the deceased, compared with what the person who died felt, we collaborated with Dr Irene Higginson of University College, London, on a study in which she was interviewing patients dying of cancer. This was part of a study of specialist support teams for nurses providing terminal cancer care. The study, we felt, might throw light on our methodological problems as well as provide the support teams with data that would help them evaluate their efforts. Once again the study was confined to deaths from cancer whereas our main study covered a random sample of all adult deaths.

Dying patients were interviewed by Dr Higginson or an assistant at intervals before they died, and asked questions about symptoms experienced and services received in the same way as was done on our main study. Some seven months after the death one of us (CS), or another interviewer who had worked on our study, approached the relatives for an interview in which the same questions were asked as well as a number of other questions relevant to an evaluation of the nursing support teams. The study covered 34 deaths for which both the patient and a relative were interviewed.

Comparing patients' and relatives' accounts, however, had one major problem: the variable length of time between the interviews with patients and their death. The wording of the questionnaire – and we stuck to this in order to make the results comparable to the questions on the main study – was such that symptoms and services reported by patients might have occurred at a different time in the illness from those reported by relatives. Discrepancies could be a result of this artefact. More specifically, if a patient said they did not have pain and the relative said they did, this could have been because the patient developed the symptom after being interviewed, and not to any genuine discrepancy. The patient interviews were done, on average, 7.9 weeks before death, and ranged from the week of death to 21 weeks beforehand.

If all the patients had been interviewed in the week of death, this might have solved the problem. But this would have been virtually impossible to arrange and there would have been additional problems. Some patients would have been unconscious or confused or less than willing to take part in such an exercise. Our sample would then have been smaller and more restricted. Another solution might have been to word the questions to refer to a specific period, but this would then have departed from the wording of the main questionnaire and destroyed much of the point of the exercise.

In spite of this drawback we still analysed the data to find out the extent of congruence and the direction and possible reasons for discrepancies.

Over their assessments of the care given by general practitioners the majority of both patients and relatives were generally appreciative. Congruence, however, was not high. The results are in Table 25.

Relatives were generally more critical than patients. For example one said of the general practitioner: 'He should have been more involved. He visited only once. Had he been private he'd have visited more. He should have given more support. He wasn't kind and caring and supportive.' The patient, however, made no additional comments and when asked to describe the care from the family doctor as excellent, good, fair or poor opted for 'excellent'. In another instance a daughter distinguished between the care her mother had had from her own general practitioner which she thought was poor and said she had no confidence in him and the care her mother had from the daughter's doctor who she described as 'our family doctor' and 'wonderful.' We had coded the comments about the mother's own general practitioner as that was the one the questions related to but the patient had only talked about the daughter's general practitioner whom she too thought was wonderful. One wife contrasted the care her husband had from the general practitioners and the home support team. 'The general practitioners could have done more to help. Pain relief was non-existent. No-one would listen to him. He was in such pain and the home support team were the only people who believed him.' The patient just commented that the practice size had made doctors less personal and it was difficult to see the same one each time, but he rated the care he got from the family doctor as 'good'.

In the instances where patients were more critical than relatives the only additional comments recorded by patients were 'He is easy to talk to, but I can't understand him. He's Pakistani.' and 'At the moment I'm very angry with the GP. She didn't find the problem in the first place and now she's not visiting. Before, very good and a friend.' This patient's husband said he could not find any fault with the doctor: 'My wife had great confidence in her doctor. I feel that perhaps she should have sent her for tests earlier.' The patient was critical about the time the doctor had to discuss things, the relative about the overall care.

Table 25 Congruity between patients' and relatives' assessments of care

	Praise from both	Praise by relative criticism by patient	Criticism by relative praise by patient	Criticism by both	MSC	Number of pairs
Doctor an easy person to talk to	21	1	5	1	0.04	28
Doctor has time to discuss things	19	2	6	4	0.13	31
Doctor described as very understanding*	20	1	5	7	0.36	33
Care from family doctor described as excellent or good*	22	2	5	4	0.17	33

* When the doctor was described as 'fairly' or 'not very understanding' this has been taken as criticism, similarly, if the care they got from the family doctor was said to be 'fair' or 'poor'.

Over symptoms, apart from constipation, congruence was also poor and again relatives reported more than patients. This type of discrepancy was particularly marked for sleeplessness, drowsiness, depression, loss of appetite, difficulty swallowing, vomiting or feeling sick, bad temper and bed sores. In our main study loss of appetite, difficulty swallowing, vomiting or feeling sick and bed sores were symptoms that were relatively often reported as developing within the last month of life: the proportions that did so were 18%, 21%, 26% and 32% respectively, compared with 10% of the other symptoms asked about in the validation exercise. For six symptoms – pain, trouble with breathing, cough, dry mouth or thirst, constipation and dizziness – discrepancies were roughly equally divided in the two directions. The data are in Table 26.

Table 26 Congruence between patients' and relatives' reports of symptoms 'in the last twelve months'

	Reported by				Number
	Both	Patient only	Relative only	Neither	MSC	of pairs
Pain	26	2	3	2	0.13	33
Trouble with breathing	10	7	5	10	0.07	32
Sleeplessness	9	6	11	5	0.01	31
Drowsiness	13	3	12	3	0.00	31
Cough	4	7	6	16	0.01	33
Dry mouth/thirst	19	6	4	2	0.01	31
Depression	4	4	12	7	0.02	27
Loss of appetite	17	1	9	4	0.11	31
Difficulty swallowing	5	2	9	14	0.08	30
Constipation	24	1	1	6	0.67	32
Vomiting or feeling sick	10	0	13	8	0.17	31
Dizziness	5	5	7	10	0.01	27
Bad temper	1	1	11	13	0.00	26
Bed sores	5	0	12	15	0.16	32

For several symptoms the numbers about which information was available from both sources was substantially less than 34. Sometimes relatives did not know or were uncertain but the amount of 'missing data' was more than four times greater for patients than for relatives, illustrating one of the problems in interviewing patients who are very ill.

There are a number of reasons for discrepancies between relatives' and patients' reports of symptoms and assessments of care. One which has already been discussed is that relatives were describing the period up until the time of death, patients about some time before that. There will also be differences in perceptions. Although we would like to have known what patients felt about their care, their accounts at these interviews some time before their death will also have their limitations. They may have been reluctant to criticise professionals who were currently involved in their care. They may also have had reasons for exaggerating or for minimising their experience of symptoms. Because patients were interviewed while the things they were being asked about were happening their reports are likely to be more vivid, but they may be responding to an immediate situation. The memories of relatives and others may have dimmed in the time before they were interviewed but they will also be in a position to put things in perspective – although the lapse of time could also distort some recollections.

This exercise was comparing results from two sources of information. These two sources could not be used to study a random sample of deaths, as it would only be possible to include patients known to be terminally ill. And this experiment has demonstrated the difficulty in collecting information from patients known to be terminally ill in the period shortly before the death. No attempt was made in this exercise to question the patients about their awareness of dying as this was obviously inappropriate in a structured interview. So this was another gap in the information from patients.

What, if anything, has it told us about the data we have obtained from relatives? It has shown that the level of symptoms reported retrospectively by relatives after a death are in general somewhat higher than the level reported by patients some time before their death. In addition, the level of criticism of care by relatives is greater than that from patients. We are relieved that the discrepancy is in that direction. It would be disconcerting to find that many patients voiced criticisms that were not recognised or reported by relatives. And obviously relatives' perceptions of the care given to the people who died are relevant. They may have been more aware of some of the things that were happening and of other things that might have been done than patients, some of whom were confused, tired and inarticulate. Obviously a patient's perceptions of symptoms are important, but so too, in terms of distress while the person is dying and for subsequent memories, are the perceptions of concerned relatives.

Both are relevant to an assessment of the adequacy and appropriateness of care.

We understand that this exercise has provided useful data in helping the support team to validate their services. We think it has also been helpful in assessing our data.

Conclusions

These various comparisons and analyses have revealed a number of strengths and weaknesses in our data. Comparisons with the information from death registration forms suggest that when people have a sudden injury or heart attack the interview data about place of death may be more realistic than that recorded on the death registration forms which apparently inflate the number of deaths occurring in hospital. In addition, to get accurate information about deaths in residential or nursing homes or even hospices from the registration forms local knowledge is needed. Our interviewer data on this is better than our inexpert classification of death registration data.

On the other hand over cause of death information recorded on the death registration form and coded by OPCS is clearly preferable to that recorded at our interviews and coded here in spite of the many problems of the former (Ashley et al, in press). A single cause of death is often unrealistic as many of the people who die are old and have more than one condition which contributes to their death. But for analyses on the study we will be using the single cause coded by OPCS on the death registration form.

The analyses of data from different types of respondents indicate that we must be wary in interpreting the relatively uncritical responses of staff in residential and nursing homes, but in general we found the results of these analyses encouraging in that many of the variations that were observed seemed to be attributable to the different circumstances of the patients the respondents were reporting about.

Less encouraging was the lack of congruity between our initial respondents and both consultants and district nurses over various procedures and care given to the people who died. The data about the procedures from all sources must be treated with scepticism.

Finally, our attempt to validate information from interviews with relatives some time after the death with data from patients some time beforehand has demonstrated the almost insuperable problems of collecting systematic data from patients, even those known to be terminally ill, in the period shortly before death. In addition, the comparisons between the two sources of data show no definite directional bias for a number of symptoms while some others are reported more often by relatives probably because they occurred shortly before death. But the low congruence between the two sources is a matter of some concern. There were fewer criticisms from patients than from relatives of the care given by general practitioners.

10 Outcomes: writing, publishing and some results

So what has come out of the study? After discussion we decided to aim at publishing the results in journals rather than in a book as we did on the earlier study. There are positive and negative reasons for this. The argument against a book is that hard backed books have become almost prohibitively expensive for individuals and libraries are having to restrict their purchases and limit the fields they cover. The demand for books presenting the results from research studies is small compared to those used for teaching, and publishers seem unwilling to publish them as paperbacks if sales are small – a Catch 22 situation. In addition, the Institute's recent experience of having research findings published as a book is that publishers appear satisfied with limited sales and are not prepared to put much effort into advertising and promotion. Individually we do not get any royalties from our books, they go to the Institute, but naturally we want the results of our studies to be known and used.

The advantage of articles in journals is that they can be directed towards the groups we want to inform and influence – general practitioners, community nurse managers, hospice directors, hospital doctors, managers of residential homes and policy makers. At this stage we do not know how successful we will be at getting our articles accepted in the journals of our choice and some of those journals have restrictions on length which will mean that we will either have to cut down on the material we present or opt for a journal with a smaller or less relevant readership.

Another factor influencing our choice of articles rather than a book was that the data we have collected can, fairly readily, be divided up into subject areas which we hope will appeal to and interest different audiences. The way we have done this can be seen from the list of planned papers at the end of this chapter. Doing it this way created some problems of overlap and there was something of a conflict between a desire to submit papers for publication as soon as possible or wait to see how other findings might influence the points we wanted to emphasise. Another problem is that some journals, for instance the British Medical Journal, do not allow manuscripts not yet in press to be cited as formal references which may lead to a chicken and egg situation for us.

Having decided on a broad publication policy we had to put it into operation and draft, check, revise and then re-check the papers for submission.

Writing, reviewing, revising and checking

We wrote the various papers individually with some discussion and comment from the other one of us. The choice of papers depended on our personal interests: CS being particularly interested in hospices, deaths from cancer, communication and community nursing; AC in general practice, residential care and comparisons with the earlier study.

When writing the papers it was a great help that we had already drafted much of this book, so that we could draw on it when describing the methods and then reference it for further details. It was also useful in making decisions about using some parts of the data, particularly the details about procedures in hospital and the types of help given by community nurses.

At the Institute drafts of all books and most papers are circulated to our advisory committee and all research staff, then discussed at a meeting of the committee which all Institute research staff attend. Some papers, particularly if they are drafted soon after one of these meetings, are just sent to selected advisers and staff members for comment. This procedure is stimulating and challenging. On balance we have found it enormously helpful, but it has its drawbacks. We do not always agree with and accept the advice and suggestions offered. Rejecting advice, particularly detailed editorial comments, takes time and is quite a difficult and frustrating task. Advisers need to be chosen with great care and knowledge and we have been both lucky and skilled in our selection. Our advisers have given us a great deal of expert and good advice, a lot of support and much valuable time.

Checking reports is the next and extremely important stage of the research process. At the Institute all figures, statements and references are checked by a researcher who did not write the initial report. He or she goes back to the tabulations, checks that these are done on the appropriate bases and then does the relevant sums and tests of significance. References are checked at source and all statements, whether based on data from the study or on other sources, are checked. In addition, the checker has to watch out for inconsistencies both in the presentation and whether real or apparent in the figures – a particularly difficult task when checking several articles by different authors on the same data set. It is not a routine job. A good checker may challenge assumptions, query the type of tests that have been done, suggest additional analyses and sometimes contribute significantly to a report. Again it is a time consuming task. The initial writer then has to check any corrections or changes and respond to suggestions. But everyone makes mistakes and although two people can independently make the same mistake this is much less likely than one person making an error. This process is vital to the accuracy and reliability of research findings.

Not all the papers were written at the end of the study. CS did a literature review on death and dying during the planning stages of the study and this influenced some of the questions we included in the study. At an international conference on multidisciplinary aspects of terminal care in 1987, AC gave a paper on methodological problems in the evaluation of the quality of care before death, and preparing that was useful in making us think about potential indicators of quality of care and about the likely snags in our data. Neither of these papers were published but CS drew on his literature review to prepare a paper 'What happens in hospices: a review of research evidence' (Seale 1989). This was the first publication from the study but is not based on the data we collected.

Some results

Up to now we have drafted eight papers based on results from the study. These are in the process of being revised and checked, so in the review that follows findings should be treated tentatively. Results are considered under roughly the same headings as the aims of the project (see page 6) when the relevant papers have been drafted.

Changes in life and care before death 1969–1987. This comparison of results from the two studies revealed no dramatic move towards a prolongation of independent and symptom free life before death during the period between the two studies. Indeed, the higher proportion of deaths occurring at age 75 or more in 1987 had been accompanied by longer periods of mental confusion, depression and incontinence. In addition, more people were spending the last year of their lives in nursing and residential homes. For the others there had been an increase in short term hospital admissions.

In spite of the increase in institutional care the majority of people, 89% in 1969 falling to 81% in 1987, spent most of the last year of their lives at home. Among those at home the proportion living alone doubled, the proportion living with a husband or wife was similar on the two studies while the proportion living with others fell markedly. So within the home there was less support available on the later study. Alongside this, the proportion receiving assistance from home helps had more than doubled between the two studies. Nevertheless, the proportion of people felt to be in need of such help, or of more help, had not changed significantly. The proportion receiving care from district nurses was similar on the two studies but the pattern of care had changed: people received care for longer periods in 1987, but fewer had it on a daily basis. Community services have probably not increased as much as the demand for them. General practitioners in 1987 were more likely than in 1969 to perceive unmet needs for district nursing and home help services.

There was some evidence that the relationship between general practitioners and relatives caring for the people who died had improved between the two studies. But at the same time as general practitioners seem to have become more accessible to mobile relatives they may have become less so to people confined to their homes in the last year of their lives. Certainly home visiting rates to the people who died fell between the two studies, and doctors' reluctance to visit was one of the more common and significant criticisms in the 1987 study.

One dramatic change between 1969 and 1987 was the rise among people dying of cancer in the proportion thought to have known what was wrong with them and in the proportion thought to have known that they were dying. But there was no change among people dying from other causes. And in both 1969 and 1987 respondents to the interview were more likely to know the prognosis and diagnosis themselves than to think that the people who died knew them.

In 1987, as in 1969, dying was often an uncomfortable and painful process. And there remain many inadequacies in our services to alleviate the distress and create a comforting and supportive environment for the final event in our lives. Technical skills may have prolonged lives but inadequate services could make this extension a misery for both patients and their relatives.

The influence of the hospice movement. The proportion of people dying in hospices increased from less than 1% in 1969 to 2.9% in 1987 and another 4% in the recent study received some form of hospice care. Hospice services were almost exclusively confined to patients with cancer.

Numerically, the influence of the hospice movement is still small, but its ideas may have been taken up by doctors and nurses working elsewhere. Willingness to talk with patients about their illness and about dying has been a central component of hospice philosophy. Our study found that hospice patients were more likely to know that they were dying than other patients dying of cancer. However, the notable increase between the 1969 and 1987 studies in the proportion of people dying of cancer who were aware of this seemed to be because hospital doctors were more likely to tell them on the recent study. The difference remained when hospice patients were excluded from the later study. But there was some suggestion of a possible influence of hospice philosophy on other forms of care within our study areas. When areas were divided into those with larger and smaller proportions of patients receiving hospice care, more of those living in the 'hospice' areas but not receiving hospice care were thought to have known that they were dying than those in the other areas. This held for both those dying of cancer and those dying of other causes. But areas with hospice services were generally south of the Bristol–Wash line and were county rather than metropolitan areas. Clearly it is impossible to attribute a general increase in openness to a single cause and during the period between the two studies there has been a general trend towards more questioning of and less deference to people with power and authority and doctors have responded by becoming rather more willing to communicate (Lancet 1980).

Another aim of hospice care is the relief of symptoms, particularly pain control, and a comparison between hospice and non-hospice patients confined to people dying of cancer in 1987 found that pain relief was better in hospices. Over this there was no indication of any dissemination to other services within the 'hospice' areas. The comparison of people receiving hospice care with cancer patients in conventional care also showed that respondents felt the quality of both inpatient and home hospice care was better than conventional care. Hospice care also differed from conventional care in that hospice patients had fewer operations in the last year of their lives and specialist home nurses adopted an advisory and emotionally supportive approach, rather than the more practical approach of district nurses who focused on doing nursing tasks.

A comparison of the characteristics and experiences of those dying from cancer with those dying from other causes served to illustrate the limits to the relevance of the hospice approach. The medical aspects of cancer care are clearly the focus of much of the hospice approach, and the comparison showed that cancer patients tended to have shorter term but more intense symptoms and restrictions, than people dying from other causes. Long term disability and dependency, often coupled with a degree of mental confusion, were more common among the non cancer group. The communication issues, particularly those relating to discussion of the likelihood of death, were less relevant in diseases other than cancer. The 'moment of truth' was medically less clear cut, and generally occurred, if at all, quite close in time to the actual death.

Apart from these medical differences, however, the key variable determining the social aspects of peoples' experience of illness was age. Cancer tended to be a disease of a relatively young group of dying people: elderly widows with few sources of social support were more frequently in the non cancer group. People living alone, or with no immediate family were also more common in the group not suffering from cancer, and this group were rarely eligible for hospice care. A picture emerged of a group of people with few sources of support to draw upon, with consequent reliance on domiciliary services or institutional care.

The hospice movement has planned an approach and a pattern of services that are geared to the needs of cancer patients, but when services are in short supply there is a danger that a concentration on those needs may contribute to the neglect of a group with rather different but possibly even greater needs.

Institutional care of people in the last year of their lives. Over half of our sample, 54%*, died in a hospital or hospice, including 2% who spent all the last twelve months of their lives in a hospital. A further 22% were admitted to a hospital or hospice at some stage during the last year of their lives. In addition, 14% of people died in a nursing or other type of residential home and another 9% spent some part of the last year of their lives there. Twelve per cent had been in a residential home for a year or more before they died. But while institutions play a part in the care of most people before they die less than a fifth of the people who died, 19%, had spent six months or more of the last year of their lives in an institution, but 35% had had some difficulty with various aspects of caring for themselves for a year or more before they died.

Up to now we have not looked in any detail at hospital care, so the rest of this section is related to care in residential homes. In contrast to hospices, residential homes cared disproportionately for older people, women, the single, the widowed, those with no living broth-

* Based on interview data.

ers or sisters and those who died from respiratory disease or from cerebrovascular accidents.

The symptoms that were more common among those in residential homes, particularly confusion, incontinence and bad temper, indicate some of the problems in making these homes attractive and stimulating places to live.

People living in residential homes were less likely than others either to die in hospital or to be admitted during the last year of their lives. Such homes seem to cut down the demand for hospital care. They probably also reduce the need for it, but this is less certain. They may also reduce the demand and need for night calls from general practitioners and, taking into account the age and frailty of residents, the pressures on the district nursing service.

Although for the most part relatives and friends thought conditions in the home were 'good' rather than 'not so good', a number of their comments and descriptions indicate that circumstances were sometimes far from ideal and, whilst most residents were in fairly frequent contact with relatives and friends from outside the home, one in five of those who spent all the last twelve months of their lives in a home had either no visitors at all or less than one visit a month. Becoming old and frail can be difficult; to be also isolated from relatives and friends seems dire. The task of relieving avoidable distress and creating a caring and heartening environment in residential and nursing homes is going to be of increasing importance in determining the quality of the last year of people's lives.

Still more to do

Even when a paper has been revised, checked and submitted to a journal, we recognise that our task is not yet complete. Journals may not accept our articles or may want them changed or cut. We will probably be faced with comments from 'expert' reviewers, some of which are likely to be helpful, some to show that we have failed to make our points clearly enough – or the reviewer to read our paper carefully enough, and even some that may make us angry and frustrated if they make points with which we disagree. So there will be more revisions – and more checking – to do. And even when a paper has been accepted there will be proofs to check and we may have to cope with editing which, if any changes are made to tables, will make AC at least seethe with rage.

Then we will need to write to the relatives, general practitioners, consultants and community nurses who took part in the study and said they would like to be told the results.

Much of this work will have to be done when one of us, CS, has gone to another job and AC will be concentrating on another project. We hope that most of it will be completed before Graham Farrow's contract with us ends. CS will, however, be working in the same field and his next job could, to some extent, be seen as an outcome of this project.

Further research

As a result of an initiative by Dr Mark McCarthy, lecturer in community medicine at University College Hospital Medical School, a research project based on the methods used in Life before death has been planned and funded. The North East Thames Regional Health Authority has agreed to fund a researcher for three years to survey relatives and others who knew residents in the region who have died, using a version of the questionnaire used on our study. This will mean that districts participating in this new study will receive information about the quality of care provided by their local services, how this compares with other districts taking part, and how they compare with the national picture in 1987.

The size of this study will depend on the number of districts agreeing to take part. Each district will need to fund the interviewing costs in their area, and 250 interviews in each district will be sought, with sampling weighted towards deaths from cancer. A number of districts have shown interest, and it is on the basis of this interest that the Region agreed to fund the researcher. Clive Seale will be a consultant to the project.

The information should help local planners in deciding on the best mix of services. At present there are plans to include a costing exercise in the study so that different options – hospice or hospital, inpatient or home care – can be costed and related to the benefits derived by patients and relatives. The Department of Health has expressed an interest in funding a health economist to take on this aspect of the work.

In sum the methods used in the present study will be used to audit and inform the planning of regional services.

Footnote – papers in draft

A comparison of hospice and conventional care – CS.

Changes in life and care in the year before death 1969–1987 – AC.

A comparison of people dying of cancer and people dying of other conditions – CS.

Community nurses and the care of the dying – CS.

The role of the general practitioner in caring for people in the last year of their lives – AC.

Communication and awareness about illness and death in a random sample of dying people – CS.

The role of residential and nursing homes in the last year of people's lives – AC.

Caring for people who die: the experience of family and friends – CS.

Other papers that are planned relate to the role of hospitals; a comparison of the experiences and views of general practitioners, district nurses and hospital consultants; day centres; outpatient departments; religion; housing; the mentally confused; and those felt by relatives or friends to have lived too long or died too soon. In addition, some comparisons may also be made with data from another Institute study on the care of patients with AIDS.

Appendix

Financial information

The project grant application submitted to and approved by the MRC requested financial support amounting to £116,074, to cover the costs of the three year study.

These were for:

a) the salary and related costs of research staff   £43,261

b) the salaries of interviewers, coders and
computer operators etc.   £57,113

c) interviewers' travelling costs and printing,
postage, sampling and computing costs   £15,700

No costs were charged to the project for Dr Cartwright's time. Similarly, no charge was made for accommodation and the general expenses of the Institute. These costs were covered by the rolling grant from the DHSS referred to in page 5.

In 1988 supplementary grant approvals were made by the MRC for:

a) a six-and-a-half months' extension of the
project because of the time to get approval
from ethical committees – additional cost
for research salaries   £10,886

b) additional cost of sampling, printing and so on   £2,229

Thus the total grant amounted to   £129,189

This grant figure is increased by any rise in nationally agreed salary scales.

Actual expenditure up to 31 December 1989 amounted to £104,797 – made up as follows:

Research salaries	£ 54,305
Interviews, etc.	£ 34,958
Expenses	£ 15,534
	£104,797

So at the time of writing it looks as if we will be comfortably within our total budget.

Louis Hancock, Treasurer,
March 1990

References

Ahmedzai S, Morton A, Reid JT, Stevenson RD. (1988). Quality of death from lung cancer: patients' reports and relatives' retrospective opinions. In: Watson M, Greer S and Thomas C (eds). Psychosocial Oncology. Oxford, Pergamon Press.

Ashley JSA, Cole SK and Kilbane MPJ (In press). Health information resources UK: health and social factors. In: Holland WW, Detels R and Knox EG (eds). Oxford textbook of Public Health (2nd edition), Volume 2. The methods of public health. Oxford, Oxford University Press.

Bowling A and Cartwright A (1982). Life after a death: a study of the elderly widowed. London, Tavistock.

Cartwright A (1964). Human relations and hospital care. London, Routledge and Kegan Paul.

Cartwright A (1967). Patients and their doctors. London, Routledge and Kegan Paul.

Cartwright A (1970). Parents and family planning services. London, Routledge and Kegan Paul.

Cartwright A, Hockey L and Anderson JL (1973). Life before death. London, Routledge and Kegan Paul.

Cartwright A and Anderson R (1981). General practice revisited. London, Tavistock.

Cartwright A and Smith C (1988). Elderly people, their medicines and their doctors. London, Routledge.

Field D (1984). 'We didn't want him to die on his own' – nurses' accounts of nursing dying patients. Journal of Advanced Nursing, 9: 59–70.

Fry J (1983). Deaths and dying. Update, 27: 1706–1707.

Gilbert C, Fulford KWM and Parker C (1989). Diversity in the practice of district ethics committees. British Medical Journal, 299: 1437–39.

Hinton J (1979). Comparison of places and policies for terminal care. The Lancet, 1: 29–32.

Hinton J (1980). Whom do dying patients tell? British Medical Journal, 281: 1328–30.

Hinton J (1981). Sharing or withholding awareness of dying between husband and wife. Journal of Psychosomatic Research, 25(5): 337–43.

Hinton J (1984). Coping with terminal illness. In Fitzpatrick R et al (ed). The experience of illness. London, Tavistock.

Lancet (1980). In cancer, honesty is here to stay. The Lancet, ii: 245.

Lock, S (1990). Monitoring research ethical committees. British Medical Journal, 300: 61–62.

Longman Group Ltd (1985). The Medical Directory. London, Longman Group.

Lunt, B (1981) Terminal cancer care: specialist services available in Great Britain 1980. Wessex Regional Cancer Organisation and the University of Southampton.

Magaziner J, Simonsick EM, Kashner TM, Hebel JR (1988). Patient-proxy response comparability on measures of patient health and functional status. Journal of Clinical Epidemiology, 41, 11: 1065–1074.

Mahoney FI, Barthel DW (1965). Functional evaluation: the Barthel Index. Maryland State Medical Association Annual Meeting: 61–65.

Marshall T and Moodie P (1989). Research ethics committees revisited. British Medical Journal, 299: 1419–20.

McCusker J, Stoddard AM (1984). Use of a surrogate for the Sickness Impact Profile. Medical Care, 22, 9: 789–795.

Medical Research Council (1985). Responsibility in the use of personal medical information for research: principles and guide to practice. London, MRC.

Melzack R (1975). The McGill pain questionnaire: major properties and scanning methods. Pain, 1: 277–299.

Melzack R et al (1985). New approaches to measuring nausea. Canadian Medical Association Journal, 133: 755–761.

Morris JN, Mor V, Goldberg RJ, Sherwood S, Greer DS, Hiris J (1986). The effect of treatment setting and patient characteristics on pain in terminal cancer patients: a report from the National Hospice Study. Journal of Chronic Disease, 39, 1: 27–35.

National Hospice Study (1986). Journal of Chronic Disease, 39: 1–62.

Office of Population Censuses and Surveys (1986). 1984 Mortality Statistics. London, HMSO. Additional unpublished data.

Office of Population Censuses and Surveys (1987). 1985 Mortality Statistics. London, HMSO. Additional unpublished data.

Office of Population Censuses and Surveys (1989). 1986 Mortality Statistics. London, HMSO.

Parkes CM (1972). Bereavement: studies of grief in adult life. London, Pelican Books.

Rees WD (1982). Role of the hospice in the care of the dying. British Medical Journal, 285: 1766–1768.

Rothschild, Lord (1971) The organisation and management of government research and development. In: A framework for government research and development. London, HMSO.

St Christopher's Hospice (1987). Hospice directory. St Christopher's Hospice and National Society for Cancer Relief.

Saunders CM (1978). The management of terminal disease. London, Edward Arnold.

Seale CF and Davies P (1987). Outcome measurement in stroke rehabilitation research. International Disability Studies, 9: 155–160.

Seale CF (1989). What happens in hospices: a review of research evidence. Social Science and Medicine, 28, 6: 551–559.

Snaith RP, Bridge GWK, Hamilton M (1976). The Leeds scale for the self-assessment of anxiety and depression. British Journal of Psychiatry, 128: 156–165.

Spitzer WO, Dobson AJ, Hall J et al (1981). Measuring the quality of life of cancer patients. Journal of Chronic Disease, 34: 585–598.

Taylor H (1983). The hospice movement in Britain: its role and its future. London, Centre for Policy on Ageing.

Ward AWM (1985). Home care services for the terminally ill: a report for the Nuffield Foundation. Department of Community Medicine, University of Sheffield.

Wilkes E (1986). Terminal care: how can we do better? Journal of the Royal College of Physicians of London, 20: 216–218.

World Health Organization (1978). Manual of the International Statistical Classification of Diseases, Injuries and Causes of Death. Geneva, World Health Organization.

Wroe J (1987). 1987/88 Handbook of Community Nursing. London, Home and Law Publishing Ltd.

Index